*The Role of Speech
in the Regulation
of Normal and
Abnormal Behavior*

THE ROLE OF SPEECH
IN THE REGULATION
OF NORMAL AND
ABNORMAL BEHAVIOR

by

ALEXANDER R. LURIA, *M.D., D.Sc.*

University of Moscow

Academy of Pedagogical Sciences, U.S.S.R.

Edited by

J. TIZARD, *Ph.D.*

LIVERIGHT PUBLISHING CORPORATION

New York

Contents

Foreword

by C. A. Mace

PROFESSOR OF PSYCHOLOGY, UNIVERSITY OF LONDON

The publication of this book is to be welcomed by all psychologists in the English-speaking communities. It is a notable addition to the all too few records in that language of the important lines of research in the U.S.S.R. Professor Luria is well known to those who attend international congresses and especially well known to those who attended his Special University Lectures in the University of London in October 1957. No one who has met him has failed to be impressed by his scientific acumen or failed to succumb to the charm of his personality. This book will enable many others to enjoy the advantages of the privileged few.

Only just second in importance to research which pushes back the frontiers which divide knowledge from ignorance are investigations which through replication confirm or modify earlier findings. This book, with Dr. Tizard's prefatory note on experimental technique, should greatly assist investigations of the latter kind.

Not less important is the encouragement it will give to the promotion of unity and co-operation in the world of science which of the Worlds in the World is the least bedevilled by international politics and international tensions.

C. A. M.

Author's Foreword

This small book contains the text of three lectures given by the author at University College, London, in 1958.

These lectures were devoted to an analysis of the development of the regulatory role of the verbal system in ontogenesis and its disruption under various pathological brain conditions. They summarize investigations conducted in recent years in the author's laboratory and they broach one of the most important problems in modern psychology.

For a long time psychology has tried to achieve a scientific analysis of the most complex—volitional—aspects of behavior. Investigations have shown, however, that such an analysis was impossible so long as such behavior was viewed as an inherent attribute of psychic life. Only when these complex aspects of psychic activity are considered as operations formed in the course of the individual's social history and embodied in the complex functional systems of the human cortex, can real strides be made towards a scientific analysis of the higher forms of psychic activity. This is why the role of verbal communication, and subsequently that of the individual verbal system, in the organization of complex pieces of behavior has become a model in the light of which the formation of the most complex aspects of psychic activity can be traced with particular clarity.

The author wishes to express his thanks to Pergamon Press and in particular to Dr. J. Tizard, who undertook the trouble of preparing this small book for publication.

A. R. L.

Moscow
October, 1960.

A Note on Experimental Techniques

Some details of the actual techniques used by the Soviet workers in the studies which are summarized in these lectures may be of interest to experimental psychologists who wish to replicate or extend the investigations outlined here. A standard piece of equipment, found in many Soviet laboratories in which this type of work is being done, consists of a display panel, for presentation of the stimuli, a rubber bulb which the subject squeezes to signify his responses, and an event recorder on which the data are recorded. Paper is driven at a constant speed by an electric motor with a variable drive, the rubber bulb held by the subject being connected by tubing to a tambour, which operates a siphon-fed pen to give continuous written records of all changes of pressure on the bulb. Other pens record, alongside, the stimuli presented to the subject. A black box, with a ground glass front about eight inches square, makes a satisfactory display panel. Inside are colored lights (white, yellow, red, green or blue), two bells which differ in pitch, and a buzzer. These can be switched on and off as required by the experimenter, who sits with the apparatus in another room. An account of

11

the technique, in many ways similar to the one now in use, was given by Ivanov-Smolensky, who first developed it, in *Brain*, 1927.

As Professor Luria points out, if the subject is asked to make a manual response each time a light appears, a conditioned reflex can be quickly established even in children 4 or 5 years old, or mentally deficient children somewhat older. The simplicity of the task and the ease of eliciting a conditioned response make the technique very useful. Differentiations can be established by having the subject respond to lights of one color but not to another, or to a short signal but not to a long one; and his ability to respond to complex instructions (e.g., to press to each red light but only to every second green one) can be easily tested. The speed of stimulus presentation can also be varied, thus changing the level of difficulty of the task. Using this technique one can study the speed of formation of stable response patterns, their stability over time, the subject's ability to change from one set of responses to another (mobility, rigidity or perseveration), and the role of speech in regulating voluntary behavior.

J. T.

*The Role of Speech
in the Regulation
of Normal and
Abnormal Behavior*

The Role of Speech
in the Formation of Mental Processes

I have chosen "The Role of Speech in the Formation of Mental Processes" as the subject of my lectures with two aims in view: first, to elucidate some basic problems on which Soviet psychologists are now engaged, and secondly, to offer an exposition of facts recently obtained from experimental investigations.

One of the basic achievements of modern scientific psychology is the trend towards studying the *genesis* of mental processes, towards analyzing their *formation and evolution.* Such research can help us to ascertain the underlying mechanisms of complex mental activities and ultimately to find scientifically grounded methods of assessing human behavior.

It would not be wrong to say that the basic principle of Soviet psychology is the idea of *development,* the proposition that such mental activities as intelligent perception, purposive memory, active attention and deliberate action result from a lengthy evolution in a child's actual behavior. Soviet psychologists are guided by the idea—long since expressed by Sechenov, the founder of Russian scientific psychology—that in essence psychology must be the science that studies *the formation of mental processes.*

It would, however, be erroneous to suppose the formation of basic mental activities and forms of behavior to be an inevitable process of the maturing of a child's mental functions, or to be a process of disconnected acquisition of new links and associations.

The fact that a child's mental activities are conditioned from the very beginning by his *social relationships with adults* is of basic importance. Age-old human experience is passed on to the child by adults and, or, in man, *mastering this experience*—in which process the child acquires not only new knowledge but also new *modes of behavior*—becomes the main form of the *mental development* unknown in animals. The works of Vygotsky—an outstanding Soviet psychologist who died twenty-five years ago, and who greatly influenced the development of Soviet psychology—are based on the idea that all the most important mental activities result from the child's social development, in the course of which there arise new *functional systems* whose sources are to be sought not in the depths of the mind but in the forms of the child's relationships with the adult world. This proposition has been further developed in a good deal of Soviet theoretical and experimental research.

Indeed, the child, physically linked to his mother when in the womb and still biologically dependent on her during infancy, remains socially bound up with her for a long time. He is linked to her at first directly and emotionally, and later through speech; by this means he not only enlarges his experience but acquires *new modes of behavior* and then *new ways of organizing his mental activities.* By naming various surrounding objects and giving the child orders and instructions, his mother shapes his behavior. Having carefully observed the objects named by his mother, after he acquires the faculty of speech, the child begins to name them *actively* and thus to organize his acts of perception and his deliberate attention. When he does as his mother tells him he retains the traces of verbal instructions in his memory for a long time. Thus he learns how to formulate his own wishes and intentions independently, first in externalized and then in inner speech. He thus creates the highest forms of purposive memory and deliberate activity. What he could previously do only with adult help, he is now able to do unassisted. This fact becomes the basic law in a child's development.

All these complex mental activities, which are bound up with speech, are at first effected by means of externalized audible speech; later they gradually speed up and become the main forms of a child's mental activity.

Many psychologists, however, readily overlook the social origin of these mental processes, which is of prime importance for an understanding of their real nature, and fall to interpreting such psychological phenomena as active attention and deliberate action as being the "inherent properties of mental life" which they believe to be rooted in the depths of the mind and not in the real external forms of the child's relationships. This conception of the real nature of the higher psychological functions makes any scientific definition of their nature impossible and turns explaining their main working mechanisms into an insoluble problem. It is therefore essential not only to reach a proper definition of the nature of the higher psychological functions, but also to make a step-by-step investigation of the complex processes through which the relationships which a child effects by means of speech lead to the formation of complicated behavior patterns, or, to use Vygotsky's terminology, the process in which functions previously *shared between two persons* gradually change into the complicated functional systems in the mind which forms *the essence of human higher mental activity*. In these lectures I will attempt to expound some experimental research on the question.

II

A vital feature of the complicated functional systems formed in the course of a child's social relationships, with either externalized or inner speech playing an integral part, is that they enable man to *go far beyond the bounds of his physical capacities* and organize the well-defined forms of active deliberate behavior whose causal explanation has always baffled psychologists.

No one is surprised that a child should obey adult orders or that adult speech should so much modify a child's perceptions. Psychologists, however, were long unable to explain man's ability to focus his attention on given objects, to single out from his external environment a given stimulus whose physical properties were not necessarily stronger than those of other stimuli and might even be weaker, and indeed to inhibit his own motor activity at will and restrain his own impulses. All this is inexplicable in terms of the mechanisms of processes in innate and immanent properties of the human psyche.

All these matters become much clearer, however, if we allow for the said "properties" having been formed in the course of the child's relationships with adults and having later changed into the means of organizing the mental processes themselves.

When a mother shows a child something and says "cup," first her pointing and then the name of the object cause an essential modification in the child's perception. By the laws of temporary links, the mother's gesture and the word designating the object become secondary signals causing marked changes in the range of stimuli acting on the child. In isolating the object from its environment, the action of pointing reinforces the stimulus, making it a figure set in a ground. The word designating the object delineates its essential functional properties and sets it within the category of other objects with similar properties; it serves a complex task of analysis and synthesis for the child, and later settles into a complex system of links acting on him and conditioning his behavior.

The child's verbal relationships with adults are not confined to this, however. These relationships strike very much deeper and form fresh independently active behavior patterns in him.

It is obvious to any observer that a child not only watches his mother's index finger but soon begins to use his own to mark given objects off from the environment; not only does he perceive the words he hears, he soon begins actively naming objects. And this is what becomes the main factor in his further mental development. He makes his own use of all the principal relationship-techniques that had earlier proceeded from adults. Thus he becomes capable of *actively modifying the environment that influences him;* by using speech for himself, he alters the relative strength of the stimuli acting upon him, and *adapts his behavior to the influences thus modified.*

It is not difficult to see that with the transition to this intermediate behavior pattern the child takes the first steps towards regulating his own activities. This process has often and rightly been attributed to the speech function, which Pavlov regarded as the specific human characteristic.

Simple experiments can demonstrate how verbal associations resulting from speech gradually come to predominate and substantially modify the relative natural strength of the stimuli.

Let me cite a few examples. Behavior is, of course, always subject to the "rule of force," and in a complex stimulus the strongest component is decisive. Pavlov confirmed this proposition as regards animals, and it can also be demonstrated in human beings.

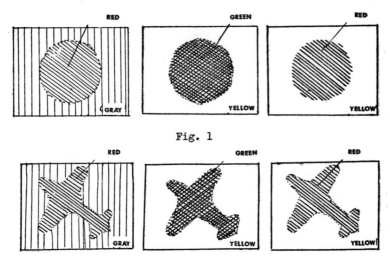

Fig. 1

Fig. 1a

If we present complex visual stimuli such as a red circle on a gray ground and a green circle on a yellow ground (Figs. 1 and 1a) to a child aged three to five, and ask him to squeeze a balloon with his right or left hand respectively when the one or the other appears, we find that after a while he has formed the habit of doing it correctly and perfectly. Similarly, it is easy to show *which element* in any complex stimulus plays the chief part and determines the response required. For this it suffices, in a control experiment, to present the child with a red circle on a yellow ground instead of gray and a green one on gray instead of yellow. Observations demonstrate that in such cases the stronger element in the compound, that is the circle, is always decisive; the child will

21

still squeeze with his right hand for the red circle and his left for the green, regardless of their backgrounds.

By means of speech, however, it is possible to alter the relative natural strength of the two elements in this complex stimulus.

Experimentation has demonstrated that this is quite possible from a certain age onwards. Let us try using speech to reinforce the weaker element in the complex visual stimulus offered to the child. If we draw his attention to the grounds on which the circles are set, and ask him to squeeze the balloon with his right hand for the gray ground and with his left for the yellow, the results obtained will vary in children of different ages. As Martsinovskaya's experiments have demonstrated, children aged three or four show no stable adaptation of their total responses. In most cases they still react to the color of the circle, which remains the stronger element in the visual compound. Children aged four or five still reveal comparatively unstable adaptation of responses, and in most cases it is only children aged five to seven who begin reacting to the background color which a verbal command has made the stronger element in the compound.

It is, however, possible to modify considerably the age at which speech affects the relative strength of stimuli; this can be done by changing the character of the verbal associations affecting the child. When, for instance, the direct verbal instructions that had not been fully effective with young children were replaced by different and more meaningful verbal instructions, the effect of speech in modifying the relative

22

strength of the visual elements began to show itself much earlier. In these experiments of Abramyan's the cultured circles were replaced by colored airplanes on the same gray or yellow grounds; the child was asked to squeeze the balloon with his right hand for a red airplane on a *yellow* ground (because "the plane can fly when the sun is shining and the sky is yellow"), and with his left hand for a green airplane on a *gray* ground (because "when it's rainy the plane can't fly and has to be stopped"). When these verbal instructions were given, the colored backgrounds of the two figures, which had been the weaker elements in the compound, took on the property of first signals, and in an overwhelming majority of cases even children of three or four began reacting to the backgrounds instead of the figures in these control experiments (Fig. 2).

These experiments show that speaking to a child can in fact re-shape its significant perception of a compound stimulus and thus modify the "rule of force" and make the physically weaker component predominate. In optimum conditions this can be achieved in quite young children.

Detailed experimental studies have shown that this modifying of the "rule of force" by speech associations may in certain conditions become not only extremely stable but also very deep-rooted, and may extend its influence to the subject's non-voluntary reactions.

In man, of course, every fresh stimulus evokes a complicated system of *orienting reflexes*, combining voluntary and involuntary (vascular, skin-galvanic, electro-encephalographic)

23

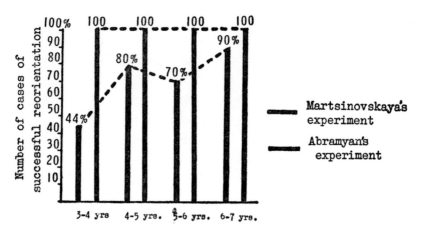

Fig. 2
The effect of experiments with the role
of words in changing the relative force of
components of a complex stimulus

motor components. These orienting reactions are, of course, also subject to the "rule of force"; their intensity roughly corresponds to that of the stimuli, and gradually declines only when these have been frequently repeated. Fig. 3 shows a change of this sort in the vascular component of an orienting reflex (the constriction of the blood-vessels in a finger resulting from the impact of stimuli of varying intensity).

As the experiments carried out in our laboratory by Sokolov and Vinogradova have shown, however, these relative natural strengths can easily be modified by influencing the subject verbally. The picture changes radically if we use verbal instruction to endow a weak stimulus with a special signaling-property (for instance, by asking the subject to press a

24

button in response to weak acoustic signals conveyed through ear-phones, or by asking him to keep count of such signals). The vascular components of the orienting reflex then become virtually inextinguishable, and it is of particular interest that the subject goes on producing stable vascular reactions to physically weak acoustic signals, and entirely fails to respond to extraneous stimuli—signals not included in the signal-system verbally defined (such as the clang of a sheet of metal thrown down outside the window). Fig. 4 shows how strikingly the normal relative strength of stimuli may be modified under the influence of speech associations.

It is only in serious pathological cases such as severe oligophrenics that a system of speech associations fails to influence the perception process or ensure a stable readjustment of the immediate relative strength of the stimuli (Fig. 5).

III

The fact that verbal instructions can modify relative natural strength is only an extreme case permitting a better illustration of the changes brought about in perception under the influence of speech associations. These changes are, however, typical of many other facts which play an important part in human psychology. They show that the influence of speech relationships may give rise to fresh functional systems distinguished by the fact that *their compound structure includes a system of speech associations* and that behavior patterns take on an active volitional character as a result.

Fig. 3

Experiment on A.S. Test 3.

The appearance of the rule of force in the vascular component of an orienting reflex when unsignalled stimuli are used

Weak sig.

Bright sig.

Bright sig.

Bright sig.

Bright sig.

metal struck suddenly and loudly

A

B

Fig. 4

Fig. 5

The orienting reflex to signal stimuli in oligrophrenic children

(A) Experiment on A.S. aged 13 (feebleminded).
Instability of the orienting reflex in motor reaction in
response to a verbally defined signal.

(B) Experiment on S.S. aged 12 (feebleminded).
Reaction to an external stimulus in the absence of reaction
to a signalled stimulus (metronome).

Soviet psychology has made a thorough investigation into many facts relating to this readjusting of perception and attention, to memorizing and imagining, to thinking and doing; the work of Vygotsky, Leontiev, Zaporozhets and Galperin, and my own researches, provide a wealth of material for analyzing the formation and structure of these functional systems. One vital fact distinguishes all these phenomena: the readjusting of mental processes under the influence of speech, and the creating of complicated forms of activity, do not happen suddenly; they are products of a long process of development, and pass through a series of stages, terminating at different points according to the type of mental activity and the complexity of the functional formations.

The simplest case of this readjusting of mental processes on the basis of speech is perhaps *the modifying of the process of forming simple temporary links under the influence of the naming-function of speech.* Important experiments in this respect have been made in Leningrad by Lyublinskaya. Children aged twelve to thirty months were given small red and green boxes, the green empty and the red containing sweets. It proved very difficult for the children to select the right boxes. If a correct choice-reaction was established, after numerous attempts, it was easily extinguished and had to be worked out afresh next day. The picture changed completely, however, when speech was brought into the experiment, that is when the experiment *named* the colors of the two boxes. The significant cue stood out boldly; the process of working out the new link was nearly three times as quick as before;

once worked out, the link proved immeasurably stronger, not being extinguished even after an interval of five days or a week; and, most interestingly, it was readily transferred to other objects (such as cups or bricks), which the child began to classify similarly.

By helping to define the required cues, speech substantially modifies the child's perception and permits the working-out of a system of stable differentiated associations. Similar experiments, perhaps even more interesting, have been carried out in Moscow by Rosengard (the results being described in her "Speech and the Development of Perception").

Although the decisive part played by speech in forming the process of visual comprehension of objects is observable even in children of eighteen months, the way speech enters into the complicated action of *generalizing* visual stimuli proves far more complex.

Experiments carried out in Zaporozhets's laboratory in Moscow have made it clear how very far speech has to develop before it becomes a real basis for elaborating complicated visual generalizations. Ruzskaya, who made a special study of this question, has developed complicated differentiated reactions in children aged from three to seven; they had to press a button with their right hands on seeing a triangle, and another with their left hands on seeing a square. Correct reactions were confirmed by the emergence of a toy car from the door of a toy garage; when the reactions were wrong, the door remained closed. Having developed correct reactions to the sight of two specific figures, the experimenter offered the child some control triangles and quadrilaterals of varying size and shape.

It was shown that it was only with great difficulty that any of the children developed correctly generalized reactions to all triangles with one hand and all quadrilaterals with the other; after numerous attempts, most of the children were unable to produce sufficiently stable generalized reactions. As soon as the experimenter offered a quadrilateral in the shape of a rhombus, a rhomboid or a trapezium, the effect of acute angles was enough to cause the wrong reaction.

Significantly, and as distinct from the above Lyublinskaya experiment, explaining the task thoroughly and naming the figures as they appeared produced no appreciable effect in small children: in these cases, as Fig. 6 shows, children aged from three to five were guided as before by immediate fragmentary impressions (acute angles), and produced many wrong reactions. Adding the figure's generalizing name to perception did not here enter into the perception system, which remained as immediate and as independent of speech as previously. Only in children aged from five to seven was any striking modification to be observed; here speech began to play a real generalizing part; perception of the figure was refracted through its generalizing name, and there were only half or one-third as many errors in this experiment as a result. The influence of speech on the development of a generalized perception of figures is thus seen to evolve much later and to be traceable in a different age-group as far as this more complicated function is concerned.

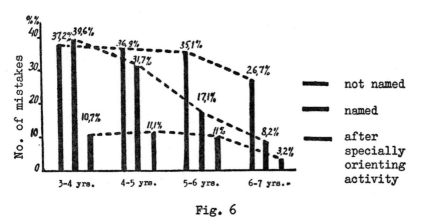

Fig. 6

The role of speech in the evolution of a generalized
perception of figures (after A.G. Ruzskaya)

Does this mean that these age-limits are irreducible, and
that forming generalized perception by means of speech is
out of the question earlier?

Ruzskaya's experiments refute this contention, and show
that forming complicated perception is perfectly possible
even in children aged three or four. It can be done only if
the child has previously been trained in the development of
successive orienting action, during which a new and generalized perception of the figure has been formed. If, before
the basic experiment, the child had taken hold of the object
in question, to feel its contours and count its angles, and had
then named it accordingly, the results changed considerably.
The figure's generalizing property had been singled out during the development of successive orienting actions, and had
been designated by an appropriate word; the result was that

31

these actions inhibited impulsive response to immediate impressions, and made it possible for generalized behavior patterns to be formed in children three or four years old. The number of wrong reactions then decreased 3.5 times. It was only later that these extended forms of orienting activity were reduced: tactile learning of the contours was replaced by visual: actual counting of the angles became superfluous, and a generalized perception of a figure named "triangle" or "quadrilateral" began to serve as a basis for direct action. Fig. 6 summarizes the results of this experiment. In this case, only an experimenter who has made a thorough study of the whole formation-process of this function can see what complex stages it has passed through before acquiring the attributes of apparent simplicity which it shows by the end of the pre-school * period.

More complicated still is the formation of a system of *connected thought that is visually concrete and also verbal*, which undergoes an even longer process of evolution and takes until an even later age.

About thirty years ago Vygotsky carried out an experiment which has exerted a profound influence on much of the subsequent work of Soviet psychologists on these problems. He would ask a child of pre-school ** age to do a simple practical task (such as drawing or tracing a picture), and would then make the task more complicated; for instance, at the moment in question, the child would find there was no pencil

* For example, by the age of seven. Editor.
** At that time, under eight. Editor.

to draw with, or no drawing-pins to hold down the tracing-paper. In this situation, there was a substantial variation in the behavior of children of different age-groups.

The very youngest—the three and four years olds—proved helpless; they could not get over the difficulty, and usually appealed to an adult for help by a verbal formulation of what was preventing their accomplishment of the task, and they did nothing until such help was given. Children aged five to seven, if given no help, tried to find a way out of the difficulty, but their behavior showed a marked change; the difficulty intensified their orientation to their surroundings, and evoked an outburst of *active speech,* addressed in part to the adult present but chiefly *to anyone:* the difficulty had caused a tremendous intensification in what at the time (when Piaget's early works had just appeared) was commonly called a child's "egocentric speech."

A thorough analysis showed, however, that this violent outburst of speech was by no means merely "egocentric" babbling; it performed a practical function and was of great help to the child in finding a way out of the difficulty. It was first a kind of *verbal orientation to surroundings,* as it were, reflecting the surrounding objects and checking the possibilities of using them to find a way out; and then it began to spread beyond the confines of the immediate situation, various systematized and generalized signs of the child's *previous experience* appearing in his "egocentric" speech.

The use of verbal links to overcome a given difficulty seems here to have played a decisive part: this showed that the child's *own speech was involved in his practical activities,* and that in applying to his own behavior the methods developed in social relationships, he had begun to form *new functional systems* in whose innermost structure speech was involved.

Nor is the nature of the speech that is incorporated into the child's active behavior accidental. At first, such speech is mainly an accompaniment to the child's practical activities, or coincides with them: but later on it begins to precede them, the child inhibiting his direct attempts until he has verbally formulated what it is he means to do. This shift from accompanying-speech to planning-speech has been discussed at length in the literature of child psychology.

The history of such speech, so important to the accomplishment of the practical task required, does not end here, however. Some time later, especially in children aged six or seven, the investigator begins to observe the *disappearance* of unattached unfocussed speech. This disappearance, however, has nothing to do with the extinction of egocentric speech and its conversion into social speech, as mentioned in Piaget's early works. In point of fact, the child's unfocussed externalized speech gradually diminishes, becomes fragmentary and appears only in the form of reduced and disconnected links, and is sometimes replaced by whispering; it thus gradually passes over into the abbreviated *internal speech* which is an invariable part of the thought-process. As electromyographic investigations carried out in Moscow by Sokolov, Novikova and Bassin have shown, it is latent in all thought, becomes activated when any difficulties arise, and is vital for orientation to difficult situations; it passes back into externalized speech only in face of especially grave difficulties or in especially severe pathological cases, of which I have made a separate study elsewhere.

Numerous other investigations carried out by various Soviet psychologists, Vygotsky's pupils and disciples, have shown this process to be *characteristic of the development of almost all the higher forms of mental activity.*

It usually begins with extensive practical activity involving extensive speech at a certain stage, and ends with the curtailment of speech at a later stage. New functional systems, including inward speech as an essential component, are thus formed. These systems are *socially generated, structurally speech-borne and by nature volitional.*

Thus observations show clearly that the incorporation of the child's own speech into his practical activity goes through various stages and terminates only at the close of the preschool period; other investigations have demonstrated, however, that by specially organizing the child's activity and including organized relationships with adults, the time needed for this development to occur can be considerably shortened.

Minskaya's recent experimental investigations at Zaporozhets's Laboratory are of particular interest here. By asking children to do various tasks connected with the practical manipulation of simple levers, she has demonstrated that children of three to four, and more especially of four to five,

Fig. 7a

after a number of attempts, can operate a simple system of levers fairly successfully to reach a goal which is inaccessible directly (Fig. 7a); but when the whole system is presented in picture form, and practical tests are therefore excluded and a solution required in concrete visual terms and discursive speech, the child is totally unable to do the task (Fig. 7b). Only between the ages of five-and-a-half and seven do children begin to tackle on their own tasks whose performance involves organized operations of imaginative kind; not till even later does it become possible for these same operations to be purely discursive, i.e., based upon verbal reasoning (Fig. 8).

The picture may radically change, however, if we apply

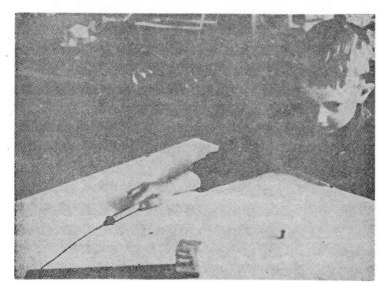

Fig. 7b

the above method of first training the child in the successive development of extended orienting actions accompanied by speech relationships.

Realizing that direct attempts did not have the desired effect, Minskaya resorted to what Soviet psychologists call "paired experiments"; the child was asked to do the task together with the experimenter or with an older child. In these experiments, not only could the child shift his attention from the final goal to the interrelation between goal and lever and fulcrum, but he could also considerably increase his orienting activities and incorporate his own speech into the process of performing the task required; he achieved this by means

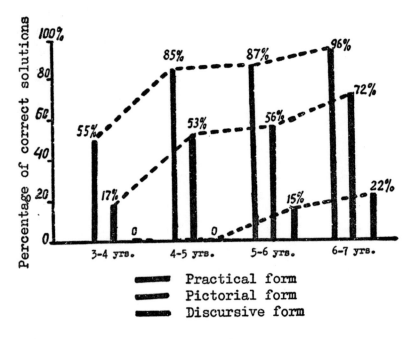

Fig. 8a

The role of speech in the formulation of practical intellectual activity. (After G.I. Minskaya)

The solution of a practical intellectual task presented in various forms

of his relationship with the adult. All this made a substantial change in his way of doing the task; his successively developing orienting actions, inhibiting his direct-impulse attempts, now played a decisive part; the operation involved his own speech, which consisted at first of interjections ("That's it!" "This way!" etc.) but later acquired the form of an extended

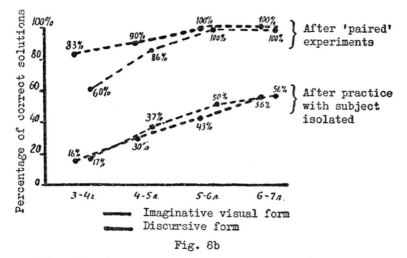

Fig. 8b

The role of speech in the formulation of practical
intellectual action. (After G.I. Minskaya)
The influence of 'paired' experiments on the
solution of a practical intellectual task

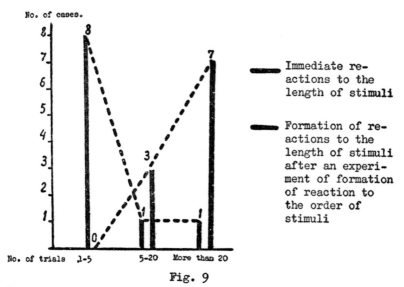

Fig. 9

The role of generalized experience in the formation of new
links

verbal analysis of the situation; his complex chain of outward movements was gradually replaced by visual examination of the levers; his speech, having arisen from his relationship to the adult, took on an independent character and was subsequently curtailed; and some time later new modes of performance were evolved which allowed him to generalize the methods acquired previously and to cope with the task not only in imaginative visual terms but also in purely verbal discursive form. The long chain of direct-impulse actions had thus been replaced by a new functional system of "mental orientation" or "direct comprehension of relationship." Those unaware of the genesis of this system may regard it as a specific higher property of the human consciousness; it is in fact, however, the product of a lengthy evolutionary development. Figure 9 summarizes the statistical results of this interesting experiment.

The above facts are of great theoretical value in that they show how scientific psychology can approach the analysis of nature and of the formation of complex psychological processes, at the same time they introduce a most fundamental practical question.

When we know that the higher psychological processes, including intellectual activity, have this complex developmental history and are formed in the course of the child's speech-based social relationships, can we continue to adhere to the former static principles in assessing a child's abilities and intellect? Can we continue to make confident judgments of a child's intellectual development merely on whether he performs a given task on his own with greater or lesser success?

Would it not be more proper to set about it differently, to reject the static principle of assessing a child's independent performance of a given task in favor of that of comparing the success of his independent performance with that achieved *with adult help?* Indeed, if the higher mental functions are in fact formed in the course of social relationships, and if today the child can do on its own what yesterday he could do only with adult help, then is it not of equal importance, and essential to prognosis, to ascertain *how far the child can make use of such help* and how he applies its results *to his independent activity* thereafter?

Some twenty-five years ago Vygotsky suggested that in assessing a child's intellectual abilities he should be asked to perform the required tasks not once but at least twice; it is also important to compare his degree of success in doing them on his own or with adult help: and then the effect of such help on his subsequent independent performance of fresh tasks should be investigated. Vygotsky called this relatively dynamic method of inquiry "the investigation of the child's zone of potential development." Children with varying potentialities will indubitably show up clearly during such an investigation, as comparative analysis of normal and of feeble-minded children has proved. Will not this method of dynamic investigation of the higher mental functions mean considerable changes in methods of practical assessment also?

IV

The formation of systems of mental process in which speech plays an integral part not only causes marked changes in the child's behavior patterns but has a substantial effect on the dynamics of nervous processes on which they are founded and *considerably modifies the basic laws of the formation of temporary links.* Pavlov declared that speech introduced "a new principle in nervous activity, that of abstracting and generalizing innumerable signals coming in from the external environment." This vital idea of the great physiologist has unfortunately been largely ignored hitherto. In his research on the work of the cerebral hemispheres Pavlov established several basic laws governing the process of creating new temporary links in animals. The chief results of his investigations are widely known, and may readily be summarized as a few fundamental propositions.

In animals, a new link is formed when a conditioned signal is accompanied by a constant unconditioned reinforcement; the evolution of the link (especially if it is fairly complicated and includes differential excitatory and inhibitory reactions) is gradual, and goes through several successive stages, from an initial generalization of reactions to similar stimuli, to a subsequent differentiation. The sequence, as Pavlov showed, is determined by a gradual concentration of highly irradiated nervous processes.

Once established, the new link becomes strong only gradually; in the earlier stages, eliminating the constant reinforcement invariably means the extinction and rapid disappearance of the link.

Moreover, a firmly established system of temporary links is highly inert, and converting it into a system of opposite links is a very difficult and often painful process for the animal. According to Pavlov, reshaping a system of conditioned reflexes in animals often means every firmly established link (both excitatory and inhibitory) having to be remade all over again by means of various fresh reinforcements.

Finally, while a system of new temporary links is being evolved, the animal always orients itself only to concrete signals and their visual relationships; when the signalling property takes on an abstract form, it often experiences insuperable difficulties. Everyone knows how difficult it is to establish in a dog conditioned reflexes to a precise sequence of signals or—as did Buytendijk and Revesz—to get an animal to react to each *subsequent* link in a chain of stimuli.

That these laws are fundamental is beyond doubt. It is noteworthy, however, that none of them applies in full force when we come to analyzing the process of the formation of new temporary links in human beings. Here the fact that any process of establishing new links uses as intermediary other links based on speech—or in Pavlovian terminology, *second signalling-system links*—plays a decisive part. These are the links that are incorporated into man's orienting activity, that abstract and systematize the signals acting on the organism, and inhibits its direct-impulse reactions. This process *creates a new information-system within which each signal presented to the subject now operates.*

We can easily prove this proposition correct if we try to reproduce in man the classical mode of establishing conditioned reflexes used by Pavlov in his animal experiments. If a child of school age, or an adult, is subjected to a given neutral stimulus, such as a red light, accompanied by a reinforcement (for instance a passive closing of the hand, or the bare order "press," as used by Ivanov-Smolensky), and if he is then presented with another light (say yellow) unaccompanied by reinforcement, we see that his behavior is never as immediate as that of animals. In a young child, the presentation of the second and differently colored signal evokes the natural question: "Shall I press for that one too?"; in an adult it at once arouses a verbal generalization formulated in inward speech as a hypothetical rule: "I am to press for a red light and not to press for a yellow"; or "I am to press for a light of any color." This adoption of a verbal rule at once modifies the nature of all subsequent reactions. Once taken into the system of verbally formulated links, the stimulus in question becomes not a mere signal but *an item of generalized information,* and all subsequent reactions depend more on the *system* it is taken into than on its physical properties.

The complex and indirect nature of temporary links in man means *a considerable modification in all their laws of evolution.*

Whereas temporary links evolve gradually in animals, in man they are as a rule formed at once by incorporating the given signal into or excluding it from an existing system of reactions. Thus the great majority of temporary links established in man under artificial laboratory conditions do not go through the stage of preliminary generalization and gradual concentration of nervous processes, but are incorporated at once into an existing category and regulated thereafter by a verbally formulated rule. This verbal-generalization system determines both the formation and the non-formation of new links; in one experiment we observed that such a generalization system resulted in adult subjects (students) proving unable to produce a differentiated reaction to signals of varying duration, even after numerous combinations: this was because the preceding experiment (pressing for every third signal) had formed in them a stable generalized tendency to watch for the rules of reaction to a given complex alternation of signals (Investigated by Shekhter) (Fig. 9).

Whereas in animals eliminating the reinforcement means the gradual extinction of the link established, no such phenomenon is observed in man; having formulated a given rule, man no longer needs the constant external reinforcement. The coincidence of the reaction with the behavior-rule as formulated now becomes the reinforcement (the "action-acceptor," to use the term suggested by Anokhin); thus man's behavior takes on the character of "the highest self-regulating system" described by Pavlov.

We have seen that reshaping a firmly established link is a very difficult process in animals; in adult humans and normal schoolchildren, however, as experiments have shown, the reinforcement of a given stimulus need be changed only once (for instance by saying "don't press" at a red light), and the whole information-system is at once modified; side by side with the conversion of the red-light property from excitatory to inhibitory, there is an immediate re-forming of the signalling property of the associated inhibitory green signal, which in the new system ("other way now") is at once perceived as excitatory.

Finally, it is not difficult to see how easily man forms systems of reactions to abstract attributes (for instance to the sequence of the signals, to alternate signals, and so on).

No one can doubt, therefore, that previously systemized experience plays a vital part in evolving new links—that this evolution takes on a new and systematic character—and that the whole dynamic of man's higher nervous processes acquires new and specifically human features—as a result of the formation of complex functional systems in which the abstracting and generalizing function of speech is an integral factor.

A thorough study of all the laws governing this specifically human neuro-dynamic is a matter for future research; but we already know some of its essential developmental features, and—particularly important—some peculiarities of its formation and derangement.

We know that the process of coupling-up new temporary links varies as between children aged two or three and five or six; and we know that in the early stages of development children's nervous processes are still characteristically very generalized and diffuse; and finally we know—and this is particularly important—that when a child's speech is just beginning to develop, it is not actively incorporated into the process of forming new links.

Thus—as various recent investigations in our laboratory, published as "Problems of Higher Nervous Activity in Normal and Abnormal Children" and especially Paramonova's research, have shown—in a young child the process of evolving a system of differentiated links frequently takes on the characteristics of forms of higher nervous activity peculiar to acts occurring without speech-participation. This process goes through preliminary generalization to gradual specialization; it needs continual reinforcement, disappears when the reinforcement is eliminated, and reaches the required level of differentiation and stability only gradually, though even then the child is often unconscious of it.

Only at the age of three-and-a-half or four does the process of evolving new links become gradually incorporated into the child's own speech; this at first takes the form of questions to an adult ("Shall I press for this light?"); then it becomes a system of independent verbal generalizations forming a given rule ("I have to press for a red light and not for a green"). At the age of four-and-a-half or five the process of evolving new links takes on all the characteristics of conscious systematic activity through the intermediary of speech, in accordance with the rules described above (Fig. 10).

The study of the ontogenesis of human higher nervous ac-

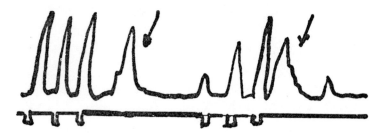

(a) simple reaction to a signal (silence)

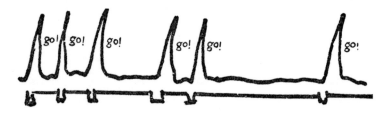

(b) do. with speech

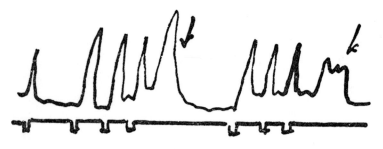

(c) do. (silence)

Lena P. 3 yrs. 6 mths.

Fig. 10

tivity is still in an initial stage of development. It is represented in Soviet science by the work of Ivanov-Smolensky, Shchelovanoc, Orbeli and Volokhov, and by various investigations made in our laboratory.

One of the basic tasks of this young science is to make a thorough study of the qualitative changes in a child's higher nervous activity from the moment speech begins to affect his active behavior, and an equally thorough analysis of the main developmental stages in the regulatory role of speech.

Subsequent lectures will deal with this problem.

The Development of the Regulatory
Role of Speech

We have seen that speech enters integrally into the structure of mental processes and that it is a powerful means of regulation of human behavior.

However, the following questions inevitably arise: how is the regulatory function of speech formed? What stages of development does it pass through? How is it converted from a means by which the adult shapes the child's behavior into the very complex mechanism thanks to which, in Pavlov's terminology, man can be considered "the highest self-regulating system"?

Let us examine these questions and by means of experimental investigations analyze the stages through which speech passes before it gradually becomes the main mechanism of conscious voluntary behavior.

I

To tackle the problem successfully one must first select a very simple model which embodies all the principal characteristics of the form of conscious voluntary regulation of behavior that interests us, and which at the same time is readily susceptible to exact and, if possible, psycho-physiological investigation.

It would not be wrong to state that *the accomplishment of a simple action on verbal instruction* can be regarded as the core of voluntary behavior regulated by speech.

There is every reason to believe that the old experiments on so-called "simple reactions," which played such a great role in the early development of experimental psychology may acquire new significance if we approach them from this standpoint.

Indeed, these very experiments with simple and complex reactions may prove very helpful in our investigation. In such cases we study reflex processes of a specific kind: they begin with the experimenter's verbal instructions, which bring about a definite conditioned connection in the child's cerebral cortex; they make the child obey precisely this conditioned connection which (throughout the experiment) must predominate over all other extraneous stimuli not included in this system. Later, in more complex forms, the conditioned connection linked to the verbal instructions can be supplemented and maintained by the child's own speech: he is able to formulate the required principle of reaction and to convert it into a regulator of his future behavior. Can a thorough, genetic analysis of the child's behavior in experiments with simple reactions allow us, therefore, to approach these experiments afresh and throw new light on them?

Let us try to uncover the real source of the phenomenon in question: let us see how the child becomes capable of subordinating his actions to the adult's verbal instructions, what forms this ability, and how, in gradually developing his ability to obey the adult's instruction, the child at the same time acquires the faculty of subordinating his actions to the connections formed *in his own speech.*

There are, in the literature, accounts of many detailed factual investigations carried out in many different countries, of the way in which the adult's verbal instruction first begins to influence the child's active behavior.

We know, from numerous Soviet studies by Shchelovanov, Rosengardt, Koltsova and others, that the adult's verbal instructions are not themselves immediately separated off from more general and direct affective forms of contact with the child. Only such verbal instructions (for instance "Give me your hands") as are uttered in a certain tone of voice as part of a definite, active situation can produce an appropriate reaction in the child. The affective and active situation as a whole still plays a decisive part at this early stage; a considerable time has yet to pass before the adult's speech becomes separated off from this situation and can call forth the required reactions in the child independently.

This very simple *impellant or initiating function of speech* may appear to develop as early as the beginning of the child's second year; it is indeed quite easy to get the required movements from a child of eighteen months by verbal instructions only, such as "Give me your hands" or "Clap hands."

Careful analysis, however, shows that the influence of this speech-function is still very limited here and that speech is quite useless when it conflicts with an action already begun. Try, for example, giving a child of twenty months to two years verbal instructions to take its stockings *off* while it is pulling them *on* (this test was made in the Shchelovanov laboratory), or to put rings *on* a bar while it is taking them *off*, and you will see that your verbal instructions are unable to alter the action already begun; on the contrary, they will merely intensify it. Thus at this stage of development the child's action still predominates: although the adult's speech has already assumed an initiating function, it cannot yet inhibit an action once started, much less *switch the child from one action to another*.

This can quite easily be analyzed by a very simple experiment.

Give a child of eighteen months to two years a rubber balloon with instructions to squeeze it. As Fig. 1 shows, the instructions readily bring about the required movement, but once having started, the child cannot *stop* the movement; the continual kinesthetic stimulation of the palm by the balloon will intensify the child's diffuse nervous excitation, and will induce further pressing movements. Though we have started the action by verbal instructions, we cannot similarly inhibit it; the added verbal instruction "That's enough" will not serve to discontinue the widely irradiating excitation process, but in many cases still further intensifies the now dominant motor-reaction system.

Thus at this early stage, while the initiating function of speech is manifestly already developed, its inhibitory function has not yet been defined. The third or preparatory function of speech, i.e., its *regulatory function proper,* is of a still more complex kind, and develops at a still later age. This function is best illustrated by a very ordinary experiment with a "simple reaction." It might seem that when we say to a child "When you see the light squeeze the balloon" we do not demand any complex form of activity. This is not so however. In actual fact such a verbal instruction is a good deal more complex than was the previous direct instruction just to squeeze the balloon. To carry it out the child has to be able to link the symbol of the future stimulus (i.e., the light) with that of the consequent response (the movement); but this movement must not be made at once but only after the real stimulus (the light) has appeared. Thus in this case the verbal stimulus *inhibits* both the direct search for the signal, and the actual movement. The essence of the instruction is that it demands a *synthesis* of the two verbal elements: it is this creation of *a preliminary system regulating a subsequent course of action* that is the principal distinguishing feature of such verbal instructions.

Can a child of eighteen months to two years, with an initiating speech-function already developed, readily subordinate his actions to such a preliminary conditioned system of verbal connections?

Yakovleva's experiments in our laboratory have shown that a child often finds that to perform such a task is beyond him.

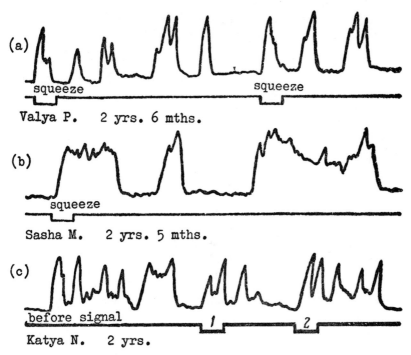

Fig. 1

Unregulated motor reactions in a child of pre-school age
Generalized action of verbal order or instruction.
(Experiments by S.V. Yakovleva)

The experiments show that in such cases the conditioned verbal instructions do not yet present a synthetic system; they still act in piecemeal fashion; the words "when you see the light" produce direct orienting reactions in the child, who begins looking for the light signal; the words "squeeze the ball" produce direct motor reactions which—owing to the conditions mentioned—become diffused and persist as a cycle of movements not controlled by speech. Because of the direct initiating action of the separate parts of the verbal instructions, the presentation of the stimulus itself (the light signal) may produce not the conditioned motor reaction of squeezing the ball, but a direct orienting reaction; the presentation of the light signal fails to take on the required signalling property, and the light begins to act as an external inhibitory agent and paradoxically causes the reaction to be discontinued (Fig. 2).

Typically, the inhibitory action of speech in such cases is incapable of producing a regulatory effect; both the generalizing verbal instructions ("Don't squeeze when there is no light") and the repeated inhibitions ("Don't squeeze, don't squeeze") will either act unspecifically and result in even more intense squeezing (Fig. 3) or will at best result in complete irradiated inhibition and the discontinuance of all motor reactions (Fig. 4).

Only through protracted and consistent training aimed at mastering each link in the verbal instructions separately, and based on practical demonstration and active reproduction of the action in question, can the connection required by the verbal instructions be formed and the child's conditioned reaction to the signal become more firmly established. Even then, however, we do not obtain a stable and distinct system of reactions to the conditioned signals. The action of squeezing the balloon persists for some time after the light has ceased to appear as a cycle of reflex movements not coordi-

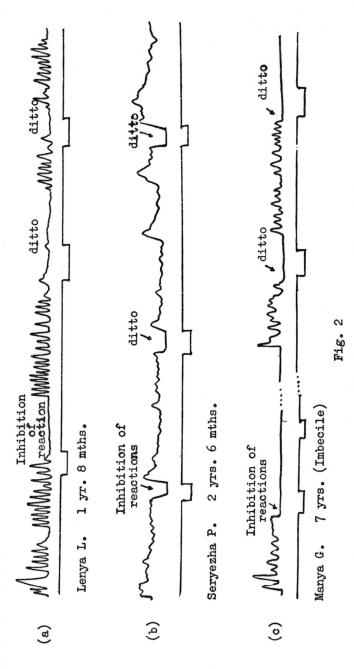

(a)

Inhibition of reaction

ditto   ditto   ditto

Lenya L. 1 yr. 8 mths.

(b)

Inhibition of reactions

ditto   ditto   ditto

Seryezha P. 2 yrs. 6 mths.

(c)

Inhibition of reactions

ditto   ditto

Manya G. 7 yrs. (Imbecile)

Fig. 2

The inhibition of motor reactions by orientation to a signal
(a) and (b) are normal children, (c) is an imbecile.

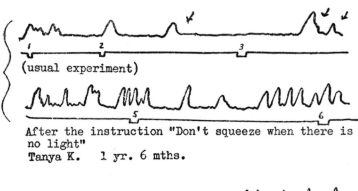

(usual experiment)

After the instruction "Don't squeeze when there is
no light"
Tanya K.   1 yr. 6 mths.

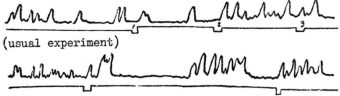

(usual experiment)

After the instruction "When there's no light, don't
squeeze - you mustn't

Olya S.   1 yr. 6 mths.

Fig. 3

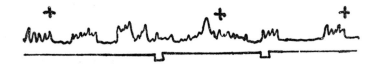

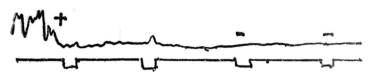

"Don't squeeze when there's no light"

Sasha M.   2 yrs. 1 mth.

Fig. 4

nated with the signal. This demonstrates the diffuse nature of the motor excitation since the child is virtually unconscious of the fact that he is continuing to squeeze the balloon and the movements remain uncontrollable (Fig. 4 shows a record of such an experiment, typical of children aged two-and-a-half to three years).

We have described the period in a child's development when his behavior is influenced solely by the very elementary initiating function of speech and when any attempt to use adult verbal instructions to inhibit motor activity already begun is unsuccessful.

Does this mean that it is quite impossible to get a young child to perform a voluntary action consisting of the inhibition of a motor action already begun and the subordination of movement to inhibitory verbal impulses? The fact that at this age the direct inhibitory function of speech is not yet developed, and that adult speech which attempts to inhibit non-volitional motor reactions often operates unspecifically and only intensifies the motor reaction, does not prevent us from seeking the beginnings of the organization of volitional movement.

Some assumptions by Sechenov, later reproduced by Anokhin, help us in tackling this problem. These scientists maintained that the inhibition of a given action usually results from conflict between two excitations, the one inhibiting the other. Is it then possible to make use of the impelling, initiating action which adult speech already has for the child, and on this basis to produce a conflict between two excitations which would result in the inhibition of the reaction already begun?

With this aim in mind, we performed a very simple experiment, the results of which fully came up to our expectations. Having failed to stop the child's continual "extra-signal" squeezing of the ball by inhibitory verbal instructions, we asked him to perform two simple actions in succession: to squeeze the ball at the flash of an electric-light signal and then move his hand away at once (for instance, put it on his knee). When he had obeyed this double set of starting instructions (which did not present any difficulty to him), we gradually reduced the distance he had to move his hand after pressing the bulb. First he was told to put it not on his knee but on the table by the ball; then we reduced the distance still further, and at last, after some time, we were able to cut out the second and intermediary part of the instructions altogether. Having learned through performing the second action to thus inhibit the first, the child was now able to cope quite easily with a task which he had previously found impossible. He was able to co-ordinate his movements strictly with the signal and no longer produced any extra-signal squeezings of the bulb. Verbal instructions, previously ineffective, could now produce the required effect, thanks to the inhibitory influences prepared by the preliminary conflict between the two successive excitations. This effect was obtained in the great majority of children aged eighteen months to two years, and in all children aged two-and-a-half to three years. Fig. 5 shows the definite effect obtained by this method.

The very fact that we have obtained the first and earliest model of organized action capable of overcoming the diffuseness of the motor impulses, cannot but encourage us in our further research. It shows once again how right Sechenov was when he regarded the voluntary movements of man as movements "acquired by learning." This impels us to continue and to intensify our work in this direction.

However, the organized movement obtained in this experiment, arose from a collision of two excitations, each of which had been called forth by the experimenter from the outside. Can we not make a new step forward and attempt to obtain a true voluntary movement—one in which the inhibition of inadequate motor impulses proceeds from the child himself.

To attempt such an experimental elaboration of an elementary voluntary act with its inherent inhibitory function it was necessary to make some basic changes in the experiment.

In the experiments so far described the verbal instructions served only as an impelling signal, while inhibitory verbal signals, to extinguish superfluous motor reactions, were not included in the experiment at all; their function was taken by the kinesthetic stimulations produced by the contractions of the muscles of the finger. It was these, in our experiment, which had to act as signals to inhibit further movements. However, we could not expect the still immature motor system of the child to ensure that these kinesthetic signals would

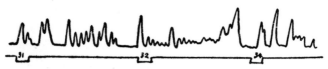

(a) Motor reaction to the signal (ball in hands)

(b) Hand moves away every time

(c) Ball in hands again

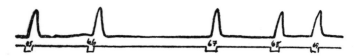

(d) do. after lengthy development of the inhibitory link (ball in hands again)

Pavel A.   2 yrs. 4 mths.

Fig. 5

Experiment with the development in infants of the inhibitory link of reaction

serve an inhibitory function as well as an excitatory one and the inhibitory function of speech also proved insufficient for this purpose. Therefore the experiment remained imperfect: receiving no distinct signal of the *fulfillment* of the task, the child did not stop its motor reactions and instead produced superfluous pressures of the bulb. We were compelled to re-shape the experiment radically and to find conditions which would bring about not only a beginning, but also an end, to the child's motor reaction. Analysis of the reflex structure of the motor act showed the way here. Many outstanding neuro-physiologists have repeatedly pointed out that the regula-tion of action requires a system of "feed-back" afferentations which give a signal for the discontinuance of the action after its accomplishment; and they have also stated that without such a system of signals, arising from the effect of the action, movement cannot become controllable. These propositions, which are accepted in present-day cybernetics, have been frequently expounded in the works of British and American psychologists and have been substantiated in Soviet physi-ology by L. A. Orbeli, N. A. Bernstein and P. K. Anokhin.

Following this line of thought is it possible to arrange our experiments in such a way as to make *the very movement of the child,* which has been initiated by the verbal instruc-tion, *produce also a distinct (and possibly exteroceptive) signal sufficient to mark the end of the action, exert an influ-ence according to the principle of "feed-back" afferentation and extinguish the irradiated motor impulses?*

To obtain such a "self-regulating" model of action, we re-

The role of a sanctioning afferentation in the execution of a voluntary movement

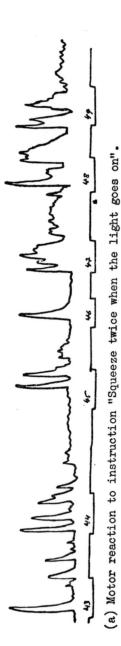

(a) Motor reactions on the instructions "Press when the light comes on!"

(b) do. with a sanctioning signal (each pressure extinguishes the lamp).

Experiment on Seryezha S. 2 yrs.

Fig. 6

(a) Motor reaction to instruction "Squeeze twice when the light goes on".

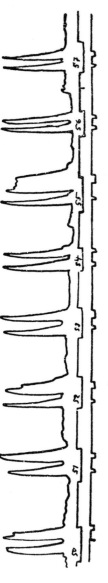

(b) do. with sanctioning signal (each squeeze causes an acoustic signal, the last signal being longer than the rest)

(c) do. but again without sanctioning signal

Experiment on Monya B. 3 yrs. 11 mths.

Fig. 6a

The role of a sanctioning afferentation in the execution of a voluntary movement

arranged the scheme of our experiment. All the conditions of the experiment remained unchanged, but the infant was instructed to press the bulb at the flash of light and thereby *to put out the light* or, in the course of a more complex experiment, to press the bulb and thereby to ring a bell. Simple mechanical devices made it possible in this way to turn off the signalling light in the first case, and to bring an electric bell into action in the second. In this experiment the stimulation of movement was not discontinued at its beginning; the very movement of the child called forth a distinct exteroceptive signal, and this signal served as a sanctioning afferentation which signalized the fulfillment of the required action.

Experiments on these lines performed by S. V. Yakovleva yielded very interesting results: in 50 per cent of all the children tested at eighteen months to two years, and in 75 per cent of children at the age of two to three years, this change in the instructions resulted in the complete disappearance of accidental intersignal pressures of the bulb and produced clear cut reactions co-ordinated with the conditioned signal (Figs. 6 and 6a); on the other hand the removal of the sanctioning afferentation led, in the overwhelming majority of children, to the recovery of the original diffusiveness of the motor reactions. Only one-third of the older children (at the age of two to three) still continued to co-ordinate their movements in time with the signals.

These experiments cannot but prove that *we have obtained the first and simplest model of a voluntary movement in a very young child.* This movement is started by verbal instruction and is stopped by visual exteroceptive signals which arise from the child's own movement. While preserving its reflex nature, it acquires all the features of a voluntary, self-regulating act. What could not be achieved through the action of the experimenter's inhibitory speech proved quite attainable through the introduction of a sanctioning signal arising from the movement. Is not this the simplest model of the self-regulating act, the analysis of which has been recently given so much attention? And does not this method of experimentation already produce an effect in children so young that one could hardly expect to obtain a real voluntary movement?

III

The obtaining of a very simple model of voluntary action in a child at the age of two to two-and-a-half opens up new prospects for our further research.

The first and simplest voluntary action of the child was regulated by an external sanctioning signal, which arose from the movement of the child itself. Is it possible, however, to ensure the organization of the experiment in such a way that self-regulation proceeds from the child itself without the help of any external regulating signal?

To this end we can quite naturally utilize the speech of the adult, which has from the first served to organize the child's behavior, and later the child's own speech. Will not both these factors help us to solve our problem and provide us with a means for the formation of true voluntary actions?

Let us recall the features which characterize both the further development of the child's ability to obey clear verbal instructions, as well as the regulatory functions of the child's own speech.

As we have already seen, at the age of three to four years substantial changes take place in the speech behavior of the child. Experience shows that an initiating system of connections can easily be established through verbal instructions in a child of three to three-and-a-half years; this can be achieved by suggesting to the child that he does not act at once but waits till the conditioned signal appears. An even more complex system of connections can be produced in this way—for example, by suggesting to the child that he press a bulb in response to a red signal and does not press in response to a green signal. However, as shown by the investigation carried out in our laboratory by N. P. Paramonova, here the excitatory part of the verbal instruction still remains considerably stronger than the inhibitory part, and the motor excitation evoked by the verbal instruction is still highly diffuse; as a rule, a child of three to three-and-a-half, will readily produce a motor reaction in response to a positive signal, but will often continue to exhibit uncontrolled inter-signal reactions. Moreover, following verbal instructions, he is able to abstain from pressing the bulb at the appearance of the inhibitory signal for only a very short time. The direct, stimulating influence of this signal is here so strong, and the inhibitory property imparted to it by the verbal instruction is so weak that it is not long before a motor reaction to the

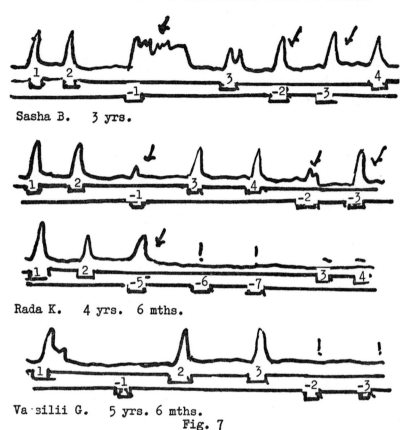

Sasha B.   3 yrs.

Rada K.   4 yrs.   6 mths.

Va·silii G.   5 yrs. 6 mths.
Fig. 7

inhibitory signal begins to appear (Fig. 7). In such cases therefore it is necessary to apply a different method and to reinforce each signal by a special verbal instruction in order to strengthen the inhibitory property of the signal and thus gradually to elaborate the required system of differentiated reactions.

Fig. 8 shows that such a task, which cannot be accomplished by preliminary verbal instruction, can easily be carried out with the help of continuous verbal reinforcement, and that the experimenter's speech which, by this time has acquired a firmly established inhibitory property, leads to the concentration of the diffuse excitation of the child and to the formation of a complete, differentiated reaction.

However, the fourth year in the life of the child, i.e., the first year of pre-school childhood, is characterized not only by the ability of the child to fulfill rather complicated instructions of the adult, but also by the fact that the child's own speech becomes rather more rich, fluent and mobile.

Can we not use this newly developed skill in the formation of further methods of instruction?

We have seen that, at the first stage of development, the regulation of the movements of the child could only be obtained when the motor reaction itself produced a distinct exteroceptive signal indicating the effect of the action; we have also seen that at the next stage of development such a regulatory influence can proceed from the sanctioning verbal reinforcement of each reaction by the adult.

But can this regulatory function be assumed by the *child's own speech?*

To answer this question, let us change once again the form of our experiment. Let us ask the child to reinforce its motor reactions by its own speech, accompanying each motor response to the signal by its own verbal command "Go!", "Go!"

Is it possible that the child's speech is now well enough

developed, and that the neurodynamic processes governing it are now sufficiently perfect to enable him to regulate his motor reactions through speech rather than through other influences of a more constant and direct nature, such as the kinesthetic stimulation proceeding from the contact with the bulb?

All attempts to make use of the regulatory role of the child's own speech at the age of two to two-and-a-half ended in failure. The speech system of children at this age is still imperfect, and to obtain even the simplest verbal reactions to conditioned signals proved impossible: moreover, such attempts impeded the organized motor reactions of the child. It is true that in these experiments children at the age of two or two-and-a-half at first reacted to the signals with the word "Go!" (or with any other phonetically simple vocal reaction); however, these reactions proved very unstable: the child soon showed himself unable to pronounce the word "Go!" and simultaneously to press the bulb. The verbal reactions either became rapidly extinct, or were produced stereotypically, without any connection with the signal; finally in some cases they began to inhibit the motor reactions by way of negative induction. Fig. 9 shows pictorially how this highly complicated task deranges organized motor reactions in children at the age of two to two-and-a-half.

Quite different results were obtained in children of three to four years, especially in those whose speech had been thoroughly trained in the kindergarten.

Unlike two-year-old children, they did not experience any

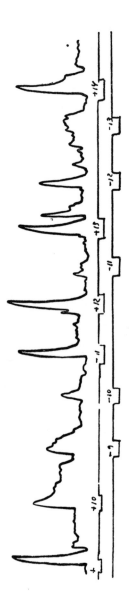

(a) The evolution of a system from a positive and inhibitory reaction to a preliminary verbal instruction

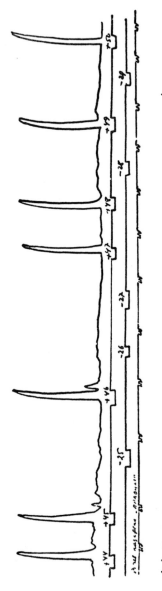

(b) Verbal reinforcement "correct!"   Do. with continuous verbal reinforcement

72

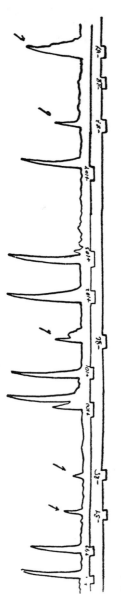

(c) Do. after cessation of continuous verbal reinforcement

Natasha B.   3 yrs. 6 mths.

Fig. 8

The development of differentiated reactions in a $3\frac{1}{2}$ yr. old child, using
verbal instruction and continuous verbal reinforcement

73

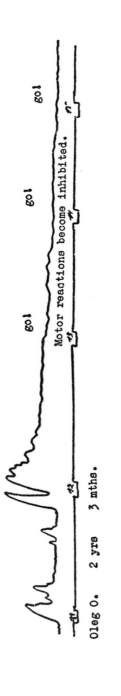

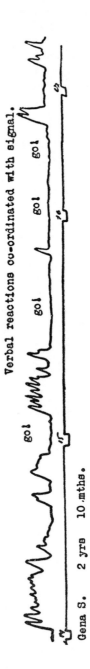

Motor reactions become inhibited.

Verbal reactions co-ordinated with signal.

go!   go!   go!

go!   go!   go!   go!

Oleg O.   2 yrs   3 mths.

Gena S.   2 yrs   10 mths.

Fig. 9

The negative influence of verbal accompaniment
of motor reactions in infants

appreciable difficulties in fulfilling the instruction to react to each signal with the words "Go!", "Go!" This task interested them greatly; their verbal reactions were always strictly co-ordinated with the signals, the latent periods being much more stable than those in the motor reactions. In contrast to the experiments demanding motor reactions, these experiments resulted in practically no perseverating verbal behavior produced independently of the signal, nor on the other hand did the responses become extinct. All the data obtained showed that *the neurodynamics of simple verbal reactions at this age become much more perfect than the neurodynamics of the motor reactions and prove to be quite concentrated and mobile.*

Is it possible, therefore, to make use of this neurodynamically quite perfect and, consequently, controllable system, to substitute it for the additional sanctioning signals, and thus obtain with its help the required regulatory effect?

Let us recall the distinct change that is produced in the course of the motor reactions by the introduction into the experiment of sanctioning exteroceptive signals; the effect of these signals becomes still more perfect and distinct in chil dren at the age of three to three-and-a-half.

Whereas, in the course of our usual experiments with motor responses produced by verbal instruction we did not succeed in extinguishing the diffuse motor reactions, the introduction of additional sanctioning signals led to their complete discontinuance. If, in our usual experiments, the child's motor reactions exhibited a direct dependence on the character of

the stimulus, as a result of which protracted stimulations produced a long tonic pressure of the bulb or repeated pressures during the entire period of action of the stimulus, the
introduction of additional sanctioning afferentation made the
movement no longer dependent on the character of the stimulus. Instead, the child began to be able to obey the verbal
instruction (Fig. 10).

However, the most essential and fundamental fact, characteristic of this stage of the child's development, is that *similar
results can be obtained if we replace the external sanctioning
afferentation by the child's own speech.* We suggest that the
child himself says "Go!" in response to each flash of light and
simultaneously presses the bulb; thereby *we replace the regulatory action of the external signal* by the child's own verbal
command, which, owing to its more perfect neurodynamics
and greater controllability, now becomes a good regulating
mechanism.

Let us cast a glance at Figs. 11 and 12 which demonstrate
the results of such experiments performed in our laboratory
by M. P. Peskovskaya and O. N. Tikhomirova. The first of
these figures clearly shows that the introduction by the child
of speech into the experiment fully eliminates the diffuseness
of the motor processes, strictly co-ordinates the movements
with the signals and imparts to them a distinct and organized
character; we can also see that with the abolition of this verbal reinforcement the motor reactions of the child again acquire a diffuse character and become poorly controlled. The
second figure shows that the introduction of the child's own

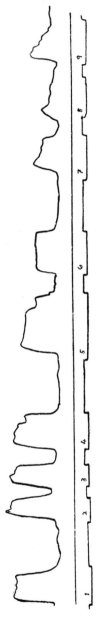

Instruction "Press when light goes on" (in silence).

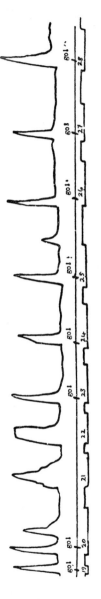

Do. accompanied by reactions to speech impulses.

Valya S.   3 yrs.

Fig. 10

The regulation of motor reactions by speech impulses

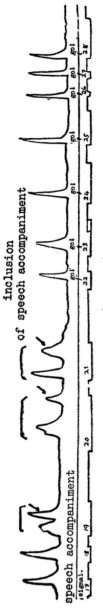
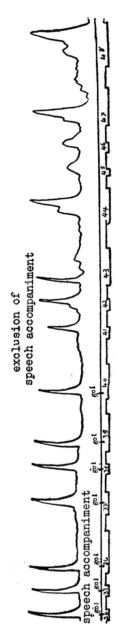

inclusion of speech accompaniment

speech accompaniment

Instruction "When a light shows, squeeze!" (silence)

exclusion of speech accompaniment

speech accompaniment

Do. accompanying squeeze with speech reaction "Go!"

Lena D. 3 yrs. 9 mths.

Fig. 10a

The regulation of motor reaction by verbal impulses

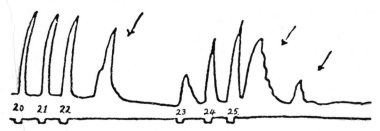

(a) Simple reactions (Speechless)

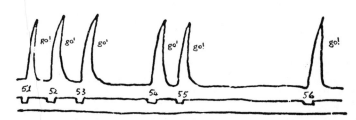

(b) do. with speech reactions go!

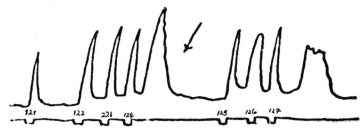

(c) do. - Speechless

Lena P.   3 yrs. 6 mths.

Fig. 11

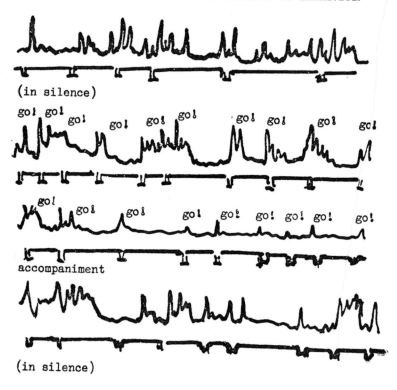

(in silence)

accompaniment

(in silence)

Olya B.   3 yrs. 9 mths.

Fig. 12

verbal reactions into the experiment puts an end to the dependence of the motor reactions on the character of the stimulus and subordinates them to the task formulated in the
verbal instruction; the child, whose motor responses during
the action of short and protracted stimuli were not of an
equally distinct character, begins to accomplish the task quite

easily; he subordinates his movement to his own abruptly pronounced command "Go!" which turns into a link between the conditioned stimulus and the reaction that controls the movements.

The regulatory role of the child's own speech can be still better illustrated, if we make our experiment somewhat more complicated.

Let us give a child of three or four years the following verbal instructions: "When the light appears, press twice!"; we will be able to see that the child is unable to cope with this task. Even knowing the meaning of the word "twice" perfectly well, the child will fulfill the task only once or twice and even then provided that the signal is not too protracted. The motor excitation produced in the child easily irradiates and no longer obeys the instruction; instead of pressing the balloon twice, the child presses it three times, four times and, finally, many times in succession. But as soon as we pass to another form of experiment in which the motor reactions to the signal are accompanied by the verbal reaction "Go!" "Go!", the irradiation of excitation stops, and the child begins to produce the required double pressures; with the discontinuance of these verbal reactions the motor reactions of the child once again acquire a diffuse character (Fig. 13).

It is difficult to overestimate the fundamental significance of these facts. In our experiments with the action of additional exteroceptive signals we succeeded in obtaining the first, although artificial, model of the simplest voluntary ac-

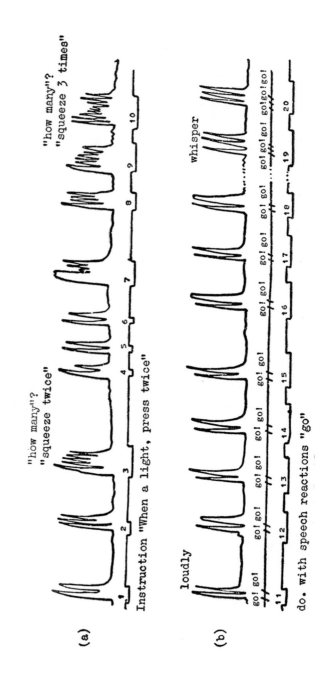

"how many"?
"squeeze twice"

"how many"?
"squeeze 3 times"

1 2 3 4 5 6 7 8 9 10

Instruction "When a light, press twice"

(a)

loudly   whisper

go!go! go!go! go!go! go!go!   go!go! go!go! go!go! go!go! go!go!go! go!go!go!

11 12 13 14 15 16 17 18 19 20

do. with speech reactions "go"

(b)

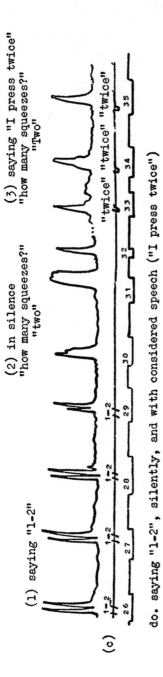

(1) saying "1-2"

(2) in silence
"how many squeezes?"
"two"

(3) saying "I press twice"
"how many squeezes?"
"Two"

do. saying "1-2", silently, and with considered speech ("I press twice")

Sasha Sh.   Experiment 12.1.56.

Fig. 13

tion of the child. But the experiments with the introduction of the child's own speech allowed us to study the *initial stages* of formation of *the natural self-regulating system* in which *the neurodynamically most perfect and developed link assumes the role of a regulating mechanism* reinforced by the verbal instruction which makes possible the accomplishment of a real voluntary act.

IV

Let us now try to characterize the mechanism which determines the regulatory influence of the child's own speech at this stage. Is this regulatory effect of the child's own speech due to the fact that the motor reactions are included in the system of elective, significative connections produced by speech, or is the influence of the child's own speech observed in the course of our experiments even more elementary, and therefore considerably more limited?

When analyzing different forms of the influence of speech we have already, at the beginning of this lecture, described the impelling or starting function of verbal instruction, as well as its inhibition and specific coupling function (or regulatory function proper). Is it possible to make use of these differentiated criteria and with their help discover which aspect of the child's own reactions performs a regulatory function in our case?

There is no doubt that the verbal reaction "Go!", which acts according to the feed-back principle, is a complex stimulus for the child itself. On the one hand, the child's subsequent behavior can be influenced by the *innervating verbal impulse* which consists in the innervation of definite speech organs and creates a center of excitation in the motor speech area of the cerebral cortex. On the other hand, it includes also the system of *elective significative connections which are called forth by speech* and which turn it into a complex signal; the latter produces a certain system of reactions already in the previous experiment shown to be closely bound up with speech. Which of these two aspects—the unspecific —impulse aspects or the specifically significative one—appears as the regulator of motor reactions at this early stage of organization of the child's behavior?

The experiments just mentioned do not provide any answer to this question. Since the impulse function and the significative function coincide in the verbal reaction of the child, it is necessary to separate them, and thus obtain an answer to the question.

A very simple method may be of help in this respect. Let us slightly alter the conditions of the experiment just described. Let us suggest to a three or four year old child, who has just successfully fulfilled the task of pressing the balloon twice in response to the signal, not to produce two separate verbal impulses—"Go!" "Go!" simultaneously, but to react to each light flash by the generalized verbal command "I shall press twice!"

It might seem that the alteration introduced by us into the experiment is insignificant. In reality, however, we have fundamentally changed the conditions of the experiment. While in the first variant the regulatory influence of the verbal reaction could proceed from two isolated impulses ("Go!" "Go!"), these two isolated impulses are now fully removed, and the regulatory influence can proceed only from the *significative* side of the self-instruction, in other words, from the elective system of connections which was firmly established by these words in the course of the previous experiment. Moreover, in the new variant of the experiment, the impulse side of the verbal self-instruction even comes into conflict with its significative side: according to the latter, the child has to press the balloon twice, while the impulse side of the words "I shall press twice!" contains only a single, protracted, innervating signal.

To what does the child subordinate his motor reaction in this case?

Experiments performed by O. K. Tikhomirov with children three to four years old produced a very definite answer to this question. If the verbal command of the child himself —"Go!" "Go!"—was a successful regulator of the motor reactions in all cases without exception, the verbal command "I shall press twice!" did not call forth the necessary effect altogether; the child, as a rule, accompanied this command by a *single protracted movement*. This clearly shows that it is the impulse aspect of speech which played a regulatory role here rather than the system of elective significative connections. Fig. 14 gives an example of the results obtained.

There is however another even more convincing experiment which shows that the regulatory influence proceeds here from the impulse side of speech, rather than from the elective connections produced by the child's speech.

Up to now we have studied the regulatory role of speech only in experiments in which a simple reaction to the signal was required, experiments that is where the verbal impulse of necessity possessed only an impelling, starting property.

We are able, however, just as successfully, to carry out experiments on *the formation of differentiated systems of connections,* in which one signal possesses a positive property and another an inhibitory one. We have already seen how difficult it is for a child of this age to inhibit its direct, impulsive reaction to a signal which, according to the verbal instruction, was to acquire a conditioned inhibitory property.

Is it possible to inhibit this impulse reaction with the help of the child's own speech, if this accompanies each presentation of the stimulus and thus reinforces its signalling property? For this purpose we could suggest to the child that each positive signal is accompanied by the word "Press!" and each inhibitory signal by the words "Don't press!"

Experiments have shown that the elaboration of such a differentiated verbal reaction to different signals does not present any difficulty to children of three or four years. However, in the light of what we have just said, the regulatory influence of such verbal reactions is in this appreciably impeded.

Indeed, the verbal reaction "Press!" accompanying each positive signal is of an impelling character both in its sig-

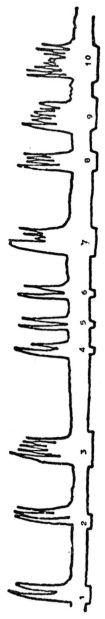

(a) Simple reaction. "When a light — press twice"

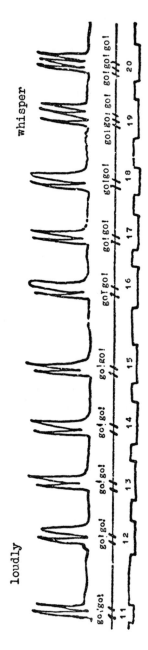

loudly   whisper

go!go!   go!go!   go!go!   go!go!   go!go!   go!go!   go!go!go!go!
   11   12   13   14   15   16   17   18   19   20

(b) do. — with speech reactions "go—go!"

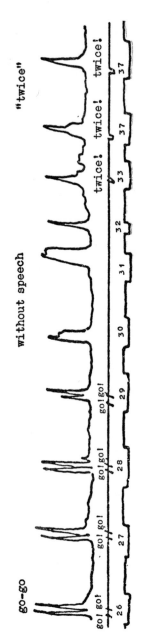

Sasha 1. 3 yrs. 6 mths.

Fig. 14

nificative and impulsive aspects. The matter is quite different with the reaction "Don't press!" which accompanies the inhibitory signals. Whereas, in its significative aspect it must be of an inhibitory character, in its impulsive aspect it still retains as well the same innervation property as the positive signal "Press!" Which side of this complex verbal reaction— the impulse side, or the significative one—will take the upper hand and influence the motor reaction? In this case, too, experiments performed with children of three to four years of age have yielded very definite results. While the verbal reaction of the child "Press!" which accompanied the positive signals, led to a concentration of excitation and produced distinct motor reactions co-ordinated with the signals, the verbal reaction "Don't press!" accompanying the inhibitory signals resulted not in the inhibition, but in the disinhibition of the motor reactions which, as shown in Fig. 15, are still further stimulated by the verbal impulse that accompanied the given signals. According to statistical data obtained by Tikhomirov, experiments on the elaboration of differentiated reactions, carried out in silence by children of three to four years of age, resulted in 42 per cent of impulsive motor reactions to inhibitory signals; but when the presentation of these signals was accompanied by the child's own verbal command "Don't press!", the number of such disinhibited reactions increased to 70 per cent.

Only when we suggested to the child that at each positive signal he should say the word "Press!" and simultaneously press the balloon, and in response to each inhibitory signal

Natasha M.   5 yrs. 8 mths

(A)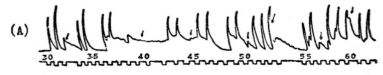

(B)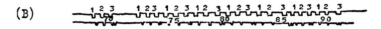

(C)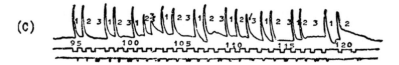

(D)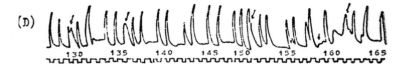

Fig. 15

The system of reactions—press the first, the second,
but not the third.
(A) in silence (B) naming the signals (C) combining
verbal and motor reactions (D) in silence

he should refrain from pressing the balloon *without uttering
a single word* was conflict eliminated: the child, previously
unable to elaborate a stable system of differentiated reactions by preliminary instruction, proved capable of attaining
it with the help of its own regulatory speech.

From this it follows that it is perfectly possible for a child
of three to four years of age to regulate his motor reactions

with the help of his own speech which reinforces the action of the preliminary verbal instruction and subsequently acts in accordance with the principle of feed-back afferentation. However, at this early stage—at least in conditions of our laboratory experiments—this regulatory influence proceeds *from the non-specific, impulse aspect of the child's own speech rather than from its elective, significative aspect.* And if by this time the non-specific influence of the speech of others is almost fully overcome in the child, it still persists with regard to the child's own speech.

V

We have considered the earliest and least investigated stages of formation of voluntary actions in the child and have described the specific and simplest forms in which the speech of the child appears as a regulatory of its behavior.

It remains for me to say a few words about the subsequent stages of development of this regulatory function of speech. The most essential feature characterizing these stages will appear unexpected to us; it is as follows: *the regulatory function is steadily transferred from the impulse side of speech to the analytic system of elective significative connections which are produced by speech.* Moreover, and this is most interesting, it simultaneously shifts *from the external to the internal speech of the child.*

Here we can manage many special experiments; but every experimenter naturally desires to investigate the genesis of the given phenomenon as thoroughly as possible, and prefers to accomplish it in one and the same series of experiments.

Experimental facts prove that the radical change just mentioned takes place in the child at the age of four-and-a-half to five-and-a-half. Before this age it is absolutely impossible to elaborate in the child a stable system of motor reactions by means of verbal instruction only. Now the child easily grasps even such a complicated instruction as "Press in response to one signal and do not press in response to the other"; it regulates its further behavior by the internally retained verbal rule, and no longer produces any impulse reactions to the signal to which a conditioned inhibitory property has been imparted. Only in those cases when the conditions of the experiment are complicated, for example, when the presentation of the signals is accelerated or the differentiation between the two signals is made more difficult, can the inhibitory stimuli still produce impulse reactions; in such cases it is often observed that the child begins to pronounce the meaning of the signal; however, the verbal reaction of the child "Don't press!" here acts not from its impulse side but from its specific significative side—it does not disinhibit the impulse reactions, but, on the contrary, inhibits them. This is why in children at the age of five to six years the introduction of a verbal reinforcement of the inhibitory signal, as shown by the experiments of O. K. Tikhomirov, halves the number of impulse reactions in these relatively complex conditions. A similar influence of the child's own external speech is observed at this age in cases when, owing to the complexity of the experimental conditions, the traces of the verbal instruction begin to lose their regulatory function. This can be clearly seen, for example, in those cases when we offer the child a difficult task, the accomplishment of which requires most complex forms of internal inhibition—say, to press twice in response to short signals and to abstain from pressing in response to long signals, or to press in response to two successive similar signals and to abstain from pressing in response to a similar third signal. The proper accomplishment of such a task often proves impossible for a five-year-old child if it tries to do it silently, merely by following the traces of the preliminary verbal instruction; however, the child proves able to cope with such a task easily if its fulfillment is accompanied by the child's own verbal reaction, which in this case reinforces the internal inhibition or fixes the sequence of the positive and inhibitory reactions.

But even in such cases a constant verbal regulation of the motor reactions is not always indispensable to normal children; it begins to play its role only in some special cases on which we shall dwell later. Therefore it often suffices to strengthen the verbal analysis of the signals presented to the child, and the internal verbal connections created by such training prove to be adequate for the further regulation of the child's motor reactions.

I have reviewed in general outline the long path of development of the regulatory role of speech in the formation of the child's behavior.

My review began at the stage when speech, being insufficiently developed, cannot serve as a regulator of the child's motor reactions; we have seen that at this stage the regulatory role is played only by the separation of the action itself, as well as by the system of practical, exteroceptive afferentations which arise from the child's own movements. It may be assumed that the system of reverse connections, developing on a practical basis and acting in accordance with the feed-back principle, is the main form of regulation of the child's behavior at the early stages of its development.

We have also considered the second stage, when the role of these external reverse signals is assumed by the child's own speech, and when the latter begins to play a regulatory role. However, we could see that at this stage the new means still acts in the old way, and that its regulatory influence in our experiments proceeds not from the system of the significative connections which are produced by speech, but from the direct, impellant or initiating action of the speech itself.

It is only at the third stage, which is characterized by the development and enrichment of the child's speech, that this "impellant" action of speech recedes into the background and the leading role passes to the regulatory influence of the system of significative connections produced by speech. This stage, however, is followed by another, final stage: the external developed forms of speech become reduced, and the decisive influence is now exerted by that higher form of internal speech which constitutes an essential component both of thought and volitional action and whose objective study still remains the task of the rising generation of scientific psychologists.

This formation of internal speech, which is closely bound up with thought, leads to a new, specifically human, stage of development. The verbal analysis of the situation begins to play an important role in the establishment of new connections; the child orients himself to the given signals with the help of the rules he has verbally formulated for himself; this abstracting and generalizing function of speech mediates the stimuli acting upon the child and turns the process of elaboration of temporary connections into the complex, "highest self-regulating system" whose peculiar properties were described in my first lecture.

Modifications in the Regulatory Role of Speech Resulting from Pathological States of the Brain

I have elucidated a number of facts relating to the development of the regulatory role of speech and its influence on the formation of voluntary movements. We have seen how the influence of speech undergoes definite changes at successive stages of the child's development and how complex elective systems of connections produced by speech, gradually acquire decisive significance in this respect.

We shall try now to utilize these data for a new approach to the *analysis of pathological changes in human activity;* we shall take the relationship between speech and action as a criterion for making out various forms of pathological behavior and for analyzing the compensation of the defects which result from it.

I

Clinical psychiatry has for many years sought to go beyond the clinical description of the changes in human behavior which result from pathological states of the brain and to discover *the physiological mechanisms,* the derangement of which leads to pathological changes. Considerable progress has been made by physiologists studying higher nervous activity as well as by psychophysiologists. They have not only made a successful approach to the analysis of the main symptoms of neuro-psychical diseases, but have also obtained with animals experimental models of neuroses and of systemic disorders of cortical activity. They have shown that almost any pathological state of the brain is inevitably accompanied by a disturbance of the principal parameters of the higher nervous processes. As a rule in these cases the strength of the nervous processes becomes markedly deranged: the co-workers and pupils of Pavlov have shown that the elaboration of systems of elective connections becomes more difficult and that these systems are highly unstable; the cortical functions become impeded owing to the transmarginal inhibition easily arising and they soon begin to reveal the effects of the phasic state under which the action of strong and weak stimuli becomes equalized; weak stimuli begin to evoke even more intense reactions than strong stimuli, and each new external agent easily disrupts the connection already established. It is easy to see that the formation of complex and differentiated systems of connection, which is peculiar to the normal activity of the brain, becomes extremely difficult in these cases.

The pathological state of the cerebral cortex often leads also to an appreciable derangement of the equilibrium of the basic nervous processes. In some cases, it is predominantly the complex processes of active inhibition which begin to suffer, and the patient exhibits symptoms of excitatory weakness which are well known to clinicians. In other cases, it is the excitatory processes which prove to be greatly affected, as a result of which the patient reacts to each difficulty with a diffused inhibitory state of the nerve cells; he manifests all the symptoms of inertness, torpidity and exhaustion, which are also well-known components of pathological states of cerebral activity.

Finally—and what is particularly important—the pathological states of the brain exert considerable influence on the third relatively less investigated property of nervous activity —the mobility of the nervous processes: they impede the rapid concentration of these processes and the transition from one state to the other opposite one. The phenomena of pathological inertness of the nervous processes which disturb the normal course of the patient's activity, have been so thoroughly described by clinicians that it is hardly necessary to emphasize their significance here for the comprehension of pathological states.

It is clear that the achievements of modern pathophysiology really help us to approach more closely the scientific analysis of the nature of pathological phenomena; if, in addition, we take into consideration the substantial progress made in recent years by clinical electrophysiology, which seeks to approach the same problems of the dynamics of the nervous processes by different methods, it will become obvious that this branch of knowledge is rapidly progressing and that in the very near future—possibly, in the lifetime of the next generation—a decisive advance towards the creation of a genuinely scientific psychopathology will occur.

However, all these achievements of scientific knowledge, showing phenomena which are common to all pathological states, are insufficient to characterize adequately the specific features of each pathological state of the brain. Only when we are able to characterize the peculiarities of each pathological state in neurodynamic concepts and to find the typical *functional units* in which the derangement of the complex, specifically human forms of higher nervous activity can be expressed, shall we approach the highly important task of medical analysis—the *differential* diagnosis of individual forms of disturbances on a pathophysiological basis.

A thorough study of the dynamics of nervous processes taking place in a normal organism may help us to find such functional units.

We know perfectly well that the dynamics of the nervous processes possess different specific features, depending on the type of functional system; for example, the neurodynamics of interoceptive processes, which are insufficiently represented in the cortex, are distinguished for their stagnant, inert character, while the neurodynamics of complex, exteroreceptive processes, which are well represented in the cortex, are much more perfect, differentiated and mobile. It goes without saying that the same distinctions are in evidence when we compare the sub-cortical synergies with the complex cortical co-ordinations, as well as when we compare, within the cortical processes, the dynamics of the old, well-established connections with dynamics of new functional systems formed during life. These facts impel us to take a new step substantially adding to the general pathophysiological characteristics of the pathologically modified activity of the brain. They lead us to attach particular importance to the characteristics of the modified neurodynamics of separate functional systems, bearing in mind that these systems may be affected to a greater or lesser degree with different lesions.

These neurodynamic characteristics of different functional systems (systems of subcortical and cortical processes, as well as systems of old and new connections) will bring us to the last and perhaps most essential question: shall we be able adequately to express the essence of the derangements of the nervous processes if we show not only the general defects in the neurodynamics but also the changes which take place in the *relationships between separate functional systems* which result from the disease and which reflect its essential features? It is a well-known fact that a severely affected system of neurodynamics easily loses its leading place, whereas the neurodynamically most intact functional system can easily retain its leading dominating character and even serve as an agent which compensates for the defects caused by the lesion. Can we find in this modified correlation between the functional systems the unit which could express the essential features of various pathological states?

Being limited by the subject of my lectures, I am unable

to dwell here on those changes in the relationships between the cortical and subcortical systems, as well as between the systems of old and new connections on which Soviet evolutionary psychoneurology based its analysis of certain pathological states.* Let me take you directly to that relationship which was the object of my own special investigation and which is regarded by me as an essential indicator for many pathological states of the brain activity. I have in mind the change in the correlation between *speech and action* or, using Pavlov's terminology, *the changed correlation between the activity of the two signalling systems* which is caused by pathological states of the brain and which can provide us with a substantial *unit* ensuring new possibilities for my analysis of pathological states.

II

It would be erroneous to think that each lesion inevitably deranges the most complex, phylogenetically younger functional systems (including speech and all connections called forth by it) and leaves intact the phylogenetically older and comparatively simpler functional formations. Such a viewpoint, which, unfortunately, has firmly established itself in science since the time of the first evolutionary investigations, can hardly be regarded as a correct one.

On the contrary, real facts convincingly show that patho-

* These aspects have been widely discussed in the Soviet literature on evolutionary psychoneurology and have been recently investigated by a number of scientists (L. A. Orbeli, L. G. Voronina, N. N. Traugott and others).

logical phenomena assume much more diversified forms: in some cases, the pathological agent deranges the older and most primitive levels of the nervous apparatus leaving the complex and youngest levels relatively unaffected: in other cases, it is the more complex levels of the functional organization which are affected most, while the more primitive and older ones remain intact. It is quite natural that in the latter group of cases the regulation of behavior by speech becomes deranged, while in the first group of cases no compensation of the arising defects is possible.

Let us begin our analysis with the first group of cases, and keep as far as possible within the limits of those facts which can illustrate the forms of disturbances taking place in the normal regulation of human behavior.

Lesions of the subcortical ganglia (we shall take for our analysis cases of Parkinsonism) gives us excellent examples of diseases which profoundly disturb the elementary components of the dynamics of the nervous processes, but do not directly affect the complex systems of cortical connections, leaving the connections of the verbal system considerably more intact and making it possible to use them as a means, to compensate to some extent for the resulting defect.

Already thirty years ago we had the occasion to deal with cases of this peculiar disturbance and to subject it to special experimental investigation.* Characteristic of these cases was the fact that pathological processes in the subcortical ganglia led to a considerable change in the tone of the pa-

* A. R. Luria. THE NATURE OF HUMAN CONFLICTS. N.Y. Liveright, 1932.

tient's movements and blocked their executive mechanism, while the cortical coupling structure of the motor act remained comparatively unaffected. It is precisely this which called forth the peculiar changes in the patient's movements: the motor impulse evoked by a certain idea rapidly involved the pathologically changed tone of the corresponding muscles and the normal synergies were deranged, as a result of which movement became impossible. However, even at that time the following paradoxical fact, well known in the clinic, attracted our attention: a patient who was absolutely unable to walk on an even floor could easily run upstairs jumping over separate steps, or more or less freely step over a number of lines drawn on the floor. In both cases the defects of the subcortical (proprioceptive) level were easily compensated by the operation of the exteroceptive mechanisms of the cortex which replaced the affected synergies by a chain of voluntary reactions to external stimuli. Thus, the operation of the unaffected cortical mechanisms proved to compensate here the defects caused by the pathological state of the lower levels.

The following question, naturally, arose before us: is it possible to make use of this phenomenon and to pass from the system of externally determined reflex movements, with the help of which we tried to overcome the defect, to a system of *self-regulated acts* formed at the level of cortical regulation? If the patient could use his unaffected coupling mechanisms—we reasoned—and produce his own signals, thereby calling forth corresponding movements, our task would be accomplished: the patient would switch over his motor act to a new, cortical system of control, and in this way to some degree compensate for his defect.

It is clear, however, that such self-signalization was as difficult for the patient as the performance of any other movement; therefore at first we used the semi-automatic, but comparatively less easily exhausting act of *winking* as such a signalling mechanism: we asked the patient to couple himself to a conditioned temporary connection in such a way as to make each winking a signal for a motor reaction. By giving the patient the instruction "Wink and press the balloon!" we obtained such a coupling: we imparted to the movement a conditioned character and switched it over to the level of voluntary cortical regulation.

Fig. 1 shows the results of this experiment. When in the course of an experiment with tapping the synergic motor reactions were fully exhausted, it proved sufficient to couple this new connection by switching over the movement to the level of cortical self-regulation, and the natural limits of the patient's residual movements were markedly extended: the patient was now able to produce a cycle of new reactions, even when previously any further synergic movement, not based on these additional afferentations, was excluded. This experiment was the fundamental factor which determined our principal methods of compensating for the above defect. However, we were still half-way from our goal. The following question arose: can we not take another step and instead of the external motor signals given by the subject to himself,

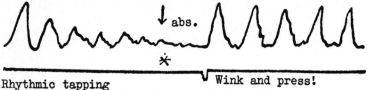

Rhythmic tapping ⌄ Wink and press!
* exhaustion of movement
Fig. 1
R. Parkinson disease (1926)
Exhaustion of motor reactions (tapping) in Parkinsonic patients and their compensation by auto-stimulation (winking)

include the defective movement of the patient into the intact system of his verbal connections? Can we turn this movement into an effector component of the complex functional system and thereby bring it to a still higher level of cortical self-regulation? If such an experiment were a success, it would terminate the cycle we had started and prove that the intact system of verbal connections could ensure a radical readjustment of the defective mechanisms and compensate for the defect at the highest of all accessible levels.

The experiment aimed at meeting these requirements was quite simple. When the movements of ordinary synergic pressures of the balloon were exhausted, we set the subject a new task, asking him to press the balloon 5 to 8 times, or— what is still more interesting—to answer the following questions by moving his fingers: "how many wheels are there on a car?", "how many brothers have you?", "how many points has the red star?", etc. In this case, the movements of the hands lost their primary character: they turned into answers

106

to verbal questions and entered the complex verbal functional system being as it were, conditioned symbolic motor responses to problems solved mentally. It suffices to cast a glance at Figs. 2 and 3 gradually showing the results of such experiments, to see the truly remarkable effects obtained by the method of including the defective subcortical synergies into the new cortical system. By adding new systems of intact, and this time verbal, afferentations to the movement, we could switch the process to a new level and attain a form of self-regulation of this process which was absolutely inaccessible when we directly attempted to intervene in the activity of the defective level of synergies.

The intact system of coupling new temporary connections enabled us to include the defective function in the system of highly complex cortical afferentations, to switch it to the level of verbal connections and thereby to compensate for the primary defect.

III

The possibility of utilizing verbal connections for the regulation of deranged behavior is not confined solely to those cases when the subcortical levels of its organization are affected. Clinical analysis shows that there are many forms of disturbances of the normal cortical activity when the system of complex verbal processes remains relatively intact and when the consolidation of verbal connections proves to be one of the most essential ways of compensating for the resulting neurodynamic defects.

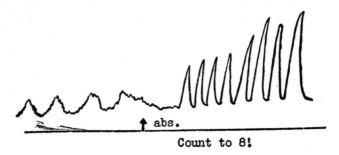

Count to 8!

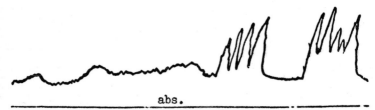

abs.

How many wheels has a car?   How many points has a red star?

Fig. 2

Organization of motor reactions in Parkinson patients by combination of verbal reactions (counting) and motor reactions

From these experiments performed thirty years ago I shall now pass to my latest experiments which take a prominent place in the research work done by our laboratory in recent years.

When studying the pathology of the higher nervous processes in children, I paid special attention to the *cerebro-asthenic syndrome*. In these cases I dealt with obvious derangements of the dynamics of the cortical processes which

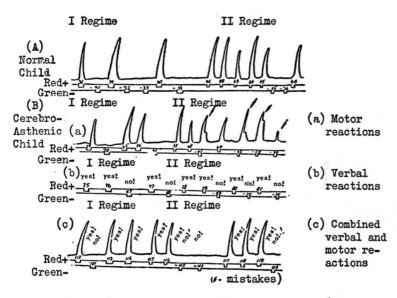

Pest. 9 yrs. 6 months. Cerebro-asthenic syndrome (after
E.D. Homskaya).

Fig. 3

The role of speech in regulation of neurodynamic defects
in cerebro-asthenic children (excitable child)

The normal child (A) and an excitable cerebro-asthenic
child (B) have to press the balloon after red signals
and to inhibit motor reactions after green signals.
After shortening and acceleration of signals (II regime)
the cerebro-asthenic child gives symptoms of disinhibition of motor reaction (a). The verbal reactions remain
adequate (b), and a combination of verbal and motor reactions (c) gives a compensation of neurodynamic defects
and a stabilization of motor reactions.

are, however, distinguished by the fact that the system of verbal connections here proves to be relatively intact—under certain conditions it can be utilized to compensate for general neurodynamic defects.

There exists a considerable number of children who reveal marked disturbances of mental development as a result of brain traumas, infections, intoxications, and sometimes early dystrophy (the latter cases were particularly widespread after the German occupation). The chief pathological agent does not call forth in such cases any irreversible disturbances of the cortical cells, but owing to disturbances in the vascular system or the cerebro-spinal fluid the normal conditions of their existence are upset. As a result, I observe appreciable changes in the general dynamics of the nervous processes, changes which are of great interest to us. Though such children are fairly normal intellectually, they become easily exhausted and soon prove unfit for normal school life. They easily lose the ability to concentrate; any extraneous stimulus distracts them from their work; they are often unable to keep pace with the class; after 5 or 10 minutes they begin to exhibit complete incomprehension of the tasks presented by the teacher and either answer the questions by guesswork, or no longer participate in the work of the class at all. Experiments have shown that the strength, degree of concentration and mobility of the nervous processes, as well as their equilibrium, prove to be markedly deranged; a thoughtful physician establishes here the syndrome of "excitatory weakness" which has long been known to the clinic and which is only now given a clearer pathophysiological interpretation.

This syndrome of cerebral asthenia can often acquire two externally different but essentially similar forms. If the pathological state of the cortical cells affects mainly the inhibitory processes, the excitatory weakness is manifested in an excessive impulsiveness of the child; each exhaustion, just as each difficult task leads to phenomena of premature reactions and to the loss by the child of any control over its own behavior. As a result, the child becomes particularly unmanageable at school. If the pathological derangement of the equilibrium of the basic nervous processes is predominantly expressed in a decline of the excitatory processes, the child begins to react to each difficulty or to each exhaustion by a sharp fall of the tone of the nervous processes: difficult questions are left unanswered, or the child falls into a state of passivity. Once again the result is exclusion from the work of the class. However, these two kinds of neurodynamic disturbances, which are well known to physicians and teachers of special schools, only testify to a decline of the strength and equilibrium of the basic nervous processes peculiar to a pathologically affected brain; while indicating a *limited* working capacity of the cerebral cells, they by no means imply any mental backwardness of these children who are only greatly weakened and highly exhaustible, but fully preserve their cognitive abilities.

The following questions naturally arise: is it possible to apply in such cases my method, i.e., to try to express the main features of this syndrome not only in general indications of the derangement of the strength and equilibrium of the nervous processes, but also in the *correlations between the verbal and motor reactions* which are peculiar to this derangement? And if the system of the verbal processes proved to be neurodynamically more intact than the system of the motor processes, will it be possible to make use of it to compensate for these neurodynamic defects?

A thorough experimental investigation carried out in our laboratory by E. D. Homskaya provides definite answers to the above questions.

If I apply the series of methods mentioned in my previous lecture, and ask a child of 9 to 11 years with the cerebro-asthenic syndrome to press a rubber bulb in response to red signals and to abstain from pressing in response to green signals (or if I elaborate such a differentiated reaction by reinforcing each red signal by the instruction "Press!" and each green signal by the instruction "Don't press!"), such an experiment will not present any appreciable difficulties to this child. It will quickly grasp the instruction, formulate the corresponding rule of action and easily accomplish the given task. However, if we somewhat complicate the neurodynamic conditions of the experiment, if we make a greater demand on the inhibitory (or excitatory) processes, the picture will radically change. For example, as soon as we pass to relatively shorter signals and present these changing signals at an accelerated rate, children of this group begin to reveal peculiar neurodynamic defects.

In children in whom the excitatory processes predominate,

these defects find their expression in the fact that any switch to an inhibitory response proves in these conditions a difficult task. Rapidly presented short inhibitory signals often call forth impulsive motor reactions. Now children of this sort are aware when they make a mistake. They often accompany incorrect responses by the exclamation "Wrong," but they are nonetheless unable to refrain from pressing the rubber bulb (Fig. 3). Such phenomena of disinhibition of inhibitory reactions are also clearly manifested in the following cases: when an accessory stimulus is presented to them (or in the presence of an external inhibitory agent which in this instance acts in a disinhibitory way); at a repeated presentation of inhibitory signals which overstrain the inhibitory processes and easily call forth a disinhibition of the delayed reaction; in conditions of protracted experimentation with a resulting exhaustion to which the child also reacts with a gradual increasing general excitation. Sometimes the disinhibition of motor reactions to inhibitory signals may occur in 50 to 60 per cent of all signals. The measurement of the reaction times enables us more profoundly to understand the mechanisms of these symptoms. When these excitable children are asked to give a number of consecutive reactions to positive signals the time taken to respond steadily decreases; this accelerating speed of reactions, which testifies to a rise of excitability and a decline of the inhibitory processes, in the end brings about premature reactions to inhibitory signals (Fig. 5).

Quite a different derangement of the neurodynamics can

be observed in *inhibitable* children with the cerebro-asthenic syndrome. Children of this group soon prove unable to respond correctly to a series of positive and inhibitory signals in relatively difficult conditions; the necessary motor responses to short positive signals begin to disappear, and further experimentation leads to a derangement of the nervous processes and often to general diffused inhibition which is accompanied by a full disappearance of any reactions both to inhibitory and to positive signals (Fig. 5). The same results are brought about by the concentration of a series of inhibitory signals, as well as by protracted experimentation leading to exhaustion. The reaction times show in this case reverse dynamics: in a series of consecutive motor reactions they steadily increase, and this gradual rise of inhibition in the end leads to the discontinuance of the required motor reactions (Fig. 6).

The above-mentioned experiments clearly characterize the neurodynamic defect which is peculiar to both groups of children with the cerebro-asthenic syndrome: they reveal those pathologically changed properties of the nervous processes which are to be compensated for in these children in the course of further experimentation.

The question now arises: how can we ensure such compensation? Is it possible to utilize for this purpose the speech system of the child? Will the inclusion of motor reactions into this system play the same compensatory role as it played in my previously mentioned experiments with patients suffering from Parkinsonism?

Reaction time
in seconds

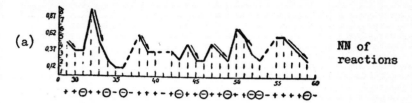

(a)

NN of
reactions

+ +⊖+ +⊖-⊖- + + +--+⊖+ +⊖+ +⊖+ +⊖⊖- + + + +⊖-

Reaction time
in seconds

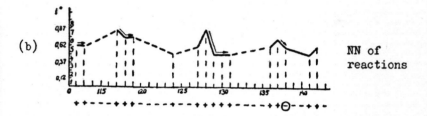

(b)

NN of
reactions

+ +--+ + +------+--+ + + + +---+⊖--+ +-

Latent periods of reactions (in seconds): + = positive
signal, - = negative signal: ⊖ = disinhibited reactions

(a) Motor reactions
(b) Combined verbal-motor reactions

Fig. 4

Dynamics of latent periods by motor and combined
(verbal-motor) reactions in excitable
cerebro-asthenic child

To answer this question, we must first of all find out to
what degree the neurodynamic defects, characterizing the
motor reactions of these children, extend to the speech system. Indeed, only when the neurodynamics of their verbal
processes prove to be more intact, shall we be able to utilize

115

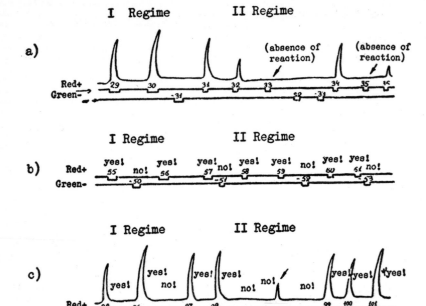

Rach. 10 yrs. Cerebro-asthenic syndrome
(after E.D.Homskaya)

Fig. 5

The role of speech in regulation of neurodynamic defects
in cerebro-asthenic children (inhibitable child)

The inhibitable cerebro-asthenic child has to press
the balloon after red signals and to inhibit motor
reaction after green signals. After shortening and
acceleration of signals (II regime) - the child
exhibits symptoms of general inhibition (motor reactions to several positive signals are missing).
(a) Verbal reactions under the same conditions (b)
remain adequate. Combination of verbal and motor
reactions (c) gives a compensation of neurodynamic
defects and a stabilization of motor reactions.

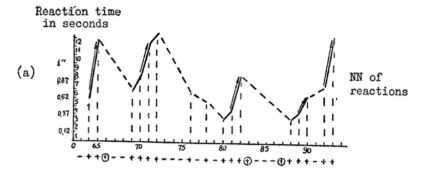

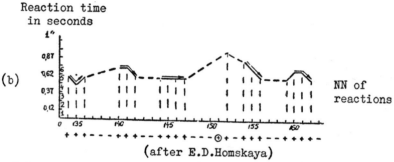

(after E.D.Homskaya)

Latent periods of reactions (in seconds): + = positive,
- = negative signal, ⊕ = failures (missing reactions)

(a) Motor reactions
(b) Combined verbal-motor reactions

Fig. 6

Dynamics of latent periods of motor and combined
(verbal-motor) reaction in inhibitable
cerebro-asthenic child

these processes as a means of compensation for the defects
so clearly observed in the motor reactions.

With this aim, we shall change the conditions of the experiment and ask the child—as we did in our previous experi-

117

ments—to react to the signals not with motor reactions, but with *verbal* ones, by saying the word "Press!" in response to the positive signals and the words "Don't press!" in response to the inhibitory signals).

Experiments carried out by E. D. Homskaya give a clear answer to our question. While in experiments with motor reactions a substantial majority of children with the cerebro-asthenic syndrome exhibited symptoms of a marked instability of the neurodynamic processes, in the new experimental conditions they invariably produced faultless and stable verbal reactions which did not disappear even after a transition to more complex conditions of experimentation—to the presentation of short signals. These experiments showed that the verbal reactions of children belonging to both groups (excitable and inhibitable) remained fully effective in all cases where the motor reactions proved to be markedly deranged; it is also characteristic that the reaction times of the verbal reactions are much more stable than those of the motor reactions and unlike the latter do not lead to any exhaustion of the excitatory processes.

These facts convincingly prove that in children belonging to this group the neurodynamics of the processes which *underly the speech system are more intact than those underlying the motor reactions;* this gives us the right to expect that a more intact speech system can exert proper regulatory influence on the deranged dynamics of the motor reactions.

To verify this fact, Homskaya applied the method already known to me: she *combined the motor and verbal reactions of the child,* by asking it to react to each signal with a corresponding verbal response and at the same time to produce the required motor reaction, or to abstain from it. If the systems of elective connections called forth by speech prove to be also intact, we may expect that the regulatory influence of the verbal responses reinforcing the conditioned property of each signal will be clearly shown.

Experiments with the combination of verbal and motor reactions performed on *excitable* children with the cerebro-asthenic syndrome have disclosed the regulatory role which is played in this case by the speech system: the combined speech and motor reactions proved to be quite stable even under those complicated experimental conditions which led to a derangement of the inhibitory reactions of the same children; the number of disinhibited reactions in these new conditions decreased from 60-50 to 15 or 10 per cent, and in some cases even to zero. But as soon as we exclude speech and pass again to isolated motor reactions, disinhibition of the motor reactions again reappears (Fig. 3a).

This analysis of changes taking place in the latent periods of the motor reactions enables us to understand some of the mechanisms which determine the influence of speech: as shown by corresponding data, the reaction times of the combined motor and verbal reactions perceptibly increase, and what is most important, become much more stable, no longer manifesting any symptoms of a mounting exhaustion of the inhibitory processes (Fig. 4a). The addition of verbal reactions to the motor ones *raises in these subjects the level of the inhibitory processes,* thereby compensating the peculiar neurodynamic defects.

The inclusion of the motor reactions into the speech system can play a similar normalizing and compensatory role in *inhibitable* children with the cerebro-asthenic syndrome.

If, in these cases, verbal and motor reactions are combined, the transition to a rapid presentation of short signals does not entail the disappearance of positive motor reactions: while responding to each positive signal with the word "Press!", the child simultaneously produces the correct motor reaction and proves able to keep in time with rapidly presented signals; but here, too, the exclusion of the verbal reactions inevitably leads to the reappearance of the previous difficulties (Fig. 5a). In this case, analysis of the latent periods shows that the inclusion of verbal reactions brings about a general acceleration of the responses and a disappearance of the phenomenon of rapid exhaustion which was observed in experiments with isolated motor reactions (Fig. 6a). Whereas in excitable children the speech system intensifies the affected inhibitory processes, in inhibitable children it exerts a modifying influence; this normalizing action of the intact and neurodynamically effective verbal connections is an indicator of the peculiar character of neurodynamic derangements which take place when the general disturbance of the nervous processes develops on the background of a relatively intact speech system which can compensate for the defect caused by the pathological process.

It is characteristic that such results may be obtained only

if the speech of the subject, included by us in the experiment, plays a practical, analyzing role separating the required signalling properties; when in our control experiments we deprived speech of this function and asked the subject to accompany each motor reaction with the words "I see!", the influence of speech acquired a reverse character, as a result of which motor reactions even to negative signals were disinhibited (Fig. 7).

The compensatory role of the speech system in cases of the cerebro-asthenic syndrome is not confined to the process of elaboration of comparatively simple systems of differentiated connections.

Experiments have shown that the inclusion of speech, as already stated above, can substantially improve both the process of *sensory analysis* and the process of *motor regulation.*

In a number of experiments performed by Homskaya two kinds of stimuli, which differed very little one from another, were presented to the children: the latter had to produce positive reactions to the flashes of a rose-colored electric bulb and to abstain from producing such reactions at the flashes of a similar, but somewhat darker bulb, or to produce positive reactions in response to protracted signals and abstain from them at the presentation of somewhat shorter signals. In both cases the difference between the positive and inhibitory signals was insignificant and was close to the threshold values.

The experiments have shown that such a delicate sensory

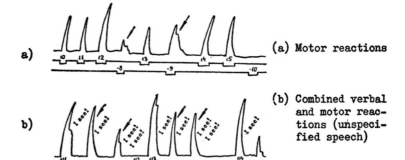

a)

(a) Motor reactions

b)

(b) Combined verbal
and motor reac-
tions (unspeci-
fied speech)

Dem. 11 yrs.   Cerebro-asthenic syndrome (⁄ =mistakes)
(after E.D.Homskaya)

Fig. 7

Disinhibition of motor reactions in cerebro-asthenic
children under the influence of non-specific speech

(a) Motor reactions to the signal: red = positive
    signal, green = negative signal (↓ = disin-
    hibition of reactions)
(b) Motor reactions combined with non-specific
    speech ("I see!"). A general disinhibition
    of motor reactions.

differentiation, which is not easy in general, proved particularly difficult for children with the cerebro-asthenic syndrome; as a rule, when the inhibitory signals were presented
several times in succession, the children began to confuse
them with the positive signals and produce motor reactions;
the subjects did not distinguish the difference between the
signals and could not realize the error they committed. However, when we changed the conditions of the experiment and
asked the child to *name* each signal (by saying the words

"Light" or "Dark," "Long" or "Short") the picture radically changed: the sensory differentiation, which could not be obtained in the case of motor reactions, now became quite possible. The introduction of the system of verbal responses acted here upon the afferent side of the neurodynamical processes, separating and fixing the distinctive properties, inhibiting the premature reactions and improving the sensory analysis. Considerable changes in the latent periods of these reactions, which were increasing and becoming more and more stable, show that the introduction of verbal reactions not only modified the structure of the actions, but also called forth substantial changes in the neurodynamics of the differentiated process.

But perhaps the most interesting experiment was that in which we, in accordance with our plan, combined the motor and verbal reactions and asked the subject to name the corresponding quality of the signal, simultaneously pressing the bulb or abstaining from such pressure. In this case, we could clearly see that *under the influence of stable and faultless verbal reactions the motor reactions also became normal and faultless* (Fig. 8). Thus, the consolidation of the delicate sensory differentiations in the two above-mentioned experiments and the intensification of the active retarding inhibition in the experiments with the differentiation of signals of longer and shorter duration could be attained by *the inclusion of the motor reactions in the regulatory verbal system.* Changes taking place in the reaction times as a result of this combination show that here the introduction of speech in-

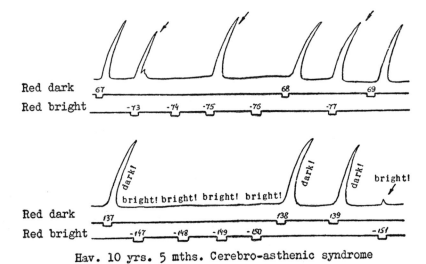

Hav. 10 yrs. 5 mths. Cerebro-asthenic syndrome

Fig. 8

The role of speech in regulation of delicate
visual differentiation

The child has to press the balloon after every dark red
signal and inhibit motor reactions after every bright
red signal. The differences in colour are minimal.
    (a) motor reactions (unstable differentiation)
    (b) combined (verbal + motor) reactions.
       (Stabilization of motor differentiation)

creases the role of active inhibition and leads to the stabilization of the differentiated analysis.

Experiments performed on children with the cerebroasthenic syndrome have disclosed the outstanding role which can be played by speech in strengthening not only the exteroceptive, but also *kinesthetic* differentiations.

124

If we ask such a child to produce a *strong* pressure of the balloon in response to a definite signal (say, a red one) and a weak pressure in response to another signal (for example, a green one), we shall see that the child will be able to cope with this task only in relatively simple conditions; but as soon as we complicate the course of the experiment, by passing, for example, to short and frequent signals, the child is no longer able to accomplish this task: the switch from strong to weak pressures is impeded by the insufficient mobility of the nervous processes. Instead of such a rapid switch, a peculiar *gradual transition* from one intensity of pressure to another, or the so-called "stairs," appear in the records; when the presentation of the signals is still more accelerated, the intensity of the pressures becomes equal.

However, experiments have shown that as soon as the speech of the subject—which even here remains intact—comes into play, and the motor reactions are combined with the verbal qualification of the required pressures ("Strong!" or "Weak!"), the picture substantially changes: the degree of concentration and mobility of the processes in the motor analyzer increase and the motor reactions acquire a strictly differentiated character (Fig. 9). Here, too, speech proves to exert a considerable regulatory influence on the neurodynamic processes, which makes it possible to obtain appreciable changes in the manifestations of the defective motor reactions.

We have described the group of pathological states of the brain in which the defects of the general neurodynamics can

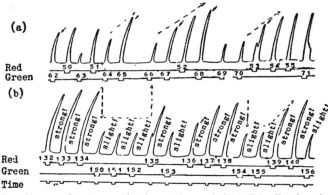

Iv. 11 yrs. Cerebro-asthenic syndrome (after E.D. Homskaya)

Fig. 9

The role of speech in establishing of motor
differentiation in a cerebro-asthenic child

The child has to press hard after every red signal and lightly
after every green one

(a) motor reactions (symptoms of protracted reshaping of reactions)
(b) combined (verbal + motor) reactions. Stabilization of motor
differentiations

be successfully compensated by the inclusion of the deranged
function into the intact verbal system.

However, it would be erroneous to think that all pathological states of the brain without exception are characterized
by a similar possibility of compensation. Even in children
with the cerebro-asthenic syndrome there are cases when,
owing to severe lesions, the dynamic of the speech system is
itself affected. No compensatory action is therefore possible.

This is especially characteristic of those cases in which the
pathological process is gross and leads to atrophic changes in

the neuron structures of the cerebral cortex, particularly affecting the complex neuron formations of the upper cortical strata, and when pathological changes in the neurodynamics first of all spread to the most complex dynamic structures on which the connection of the verbal system are based, thereby deranging the verbal processes themselves. These cases are typical of the second group of pathological states of the brain where the relationships between speech and action are substantially changed and where the pathologically modified neurodynamics of the speech system do not allow speech to be used as a regulatory and compensatory factor.

Oligophrenia is perhaps the most typical, and the most investigated, case of such lesions; it is a profound mental underdevelopment which results from a massive cerebral lesion experienced in the intra-uterine period or in early childhood and leading to a severe disturbance of the subsequent mental development of the child. In this case the lesion of the brain is not confined to a derangement of the vascular system or the C.S.F.; it brings about profound atrophic changes; the latter are particularly expressed in the underdevelopment of the complex neuron structures of the first and third strata of the cortex, which is most pronounced in the highly complex, specifically human formations of the cerebral cortex. Precisely these atrophic processes lead to a profound derangement of the cortical neurodynamics, which do not here bear a temporary and reversible character but on the contrary, are highly stationary and irreversible.

As shown by the investigations of L. A. Novikova carried

out in our laboratory, a mere recording of the electrical activity of the brain reveals in oligophrenics—in contra-distinction to children belonging to the above-described group—a profound inhibitory state of the cortex which is expressed not only in constant pathological slow waves, evenly manifested in all parts of the brain but, what is particularly important, in profound modifications of the reactive electroencephalogram. According to the experimental data of N. N. Zisslina the α-rhythm of normal children can easily be speeded up to higher frequency (from 10 or 12 to 20 or 24 oscillations per second) by means of stroboscopically produced flicker; but this is not possible in the case of oligophrenics. It is not difficult to obtain with oligophrenic children, however, a reverse switch of the α-rhythm i.e., to a lower frequency (from 10 or 12 to 4 or 6 oscillations per second), and this is never observed in normal cases. This fact, graphically shown in Fig. 10, clearly indicates that the cerebral cortex of an oligophrenic child is in a pathological inhibitory state, which differs greatly from the cerebral cortex of a normal subject.

It is quite natural that the massive changes in the cortical structures, which result in a pathological inhibitory state of the cortex, must invariably lead to a profound disturbance of the higher nervous activity in oligophrenic children and that they do not arise as a temporary phenomenon determined by strictly definite conditions, but bear a permanent and stationary character; of great importance is the fact that they affect both the active state of the cortex which is indispensable for the most complex forms of activity and the

(after Zisslina) 3.

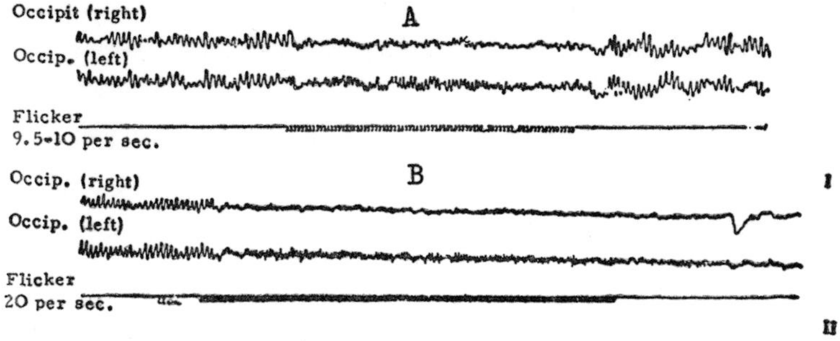

I. Normal

A Normal child, 14:0. Marked re-adaptation of the α-rhythm to the flicker 10 per sec.

B Normal child, 11:0. Marked re-adaptation of the α-rhythm to the flicker 20 per sec.

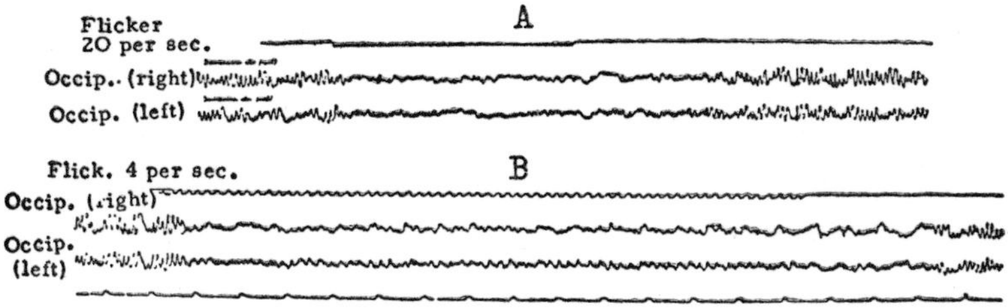

I. Oligophrenic child, 13:0

A Depression of electrical activity after flicker 20 per sec.

B Re-adaptation of the α-rhythm to the flicker 4 per sec.

Fig. 10

Electro-encephalographic reactions to flicker
in normal and oligophrenic children

separate highly complex functional systems which we utilize to compensate for the neurodynamical defects arising under the cerebro-asthenic syndrome.

Experiments performed by O. S. Vinogradova have shown that the inhibitory state of the cortex, peculiar to profound oligophrenics, is manifested both in considerable derangements of the orienting reflex (on which any active behavior is based) and in very coarse derangements of the structure of the verbal connections which constitute the basis of complex intellectual processes.

If (as it was pointed out in our first lecture) the behavior of a normal pupil or of an adult subject takes place on the background of stable orienting reflexes (in laboratory experiments this is expressed in the fact that each new stimulus invariably calls forth a constriction of the blood vessels of the arm, a skin-galvanic reaction, or depression of the α-rhythm), in a profound oligophrenic these reactions do not last long and disappear after two or three stimulations (Fig. 11) this clearly testifies to the fact that the processes responsible for mental activities develop on the background of a state of passivity.

If (as was demonstrated in a special series of experiments) the vascular reactions evoked by a certain word (for example, by the word "Cat") can be called forth in a normal pupil by some other words of a more or less similar sense, such as "Mouse," "Dog," etc., but cannot be called forth by any consonant words, such as "Hat," "Mat," and others, the irradiation of the nervous processes, peculiar to the inhibited cer-

(a) Normal child, 11.0

(b) Oligophrenic child, 10.6

Fig. 11

Plethysmographic component of orienting reflex (constriction of
the vessels of the finger) in normal and oligophrenic children

(a) Normal child. The instruction to count every metronome signal brings a stable orienting
reaction (constriction of vessels of the finger).
(b) Oligophrenic child. The same instruction does not bring a stable orienting reaction (no
constrictions of the vessels of the finger after the metronome). Only a loud bell
gives a constriction of vessels.

(after O.Vinogradova)

ebral cortex of oligophrenic children, loses its elective character; experiments performed by O. S. Vinogradova reveal here a reverse picture. Whereas in profound oligophrenics we were able to consolidate with the help of special methods the vascular reactions to the word "Cat," no such reactions could be evoked by other words of a more or less similar sense, such as "Mouse," "Dog," etc.; however, the same reactions could be called forth by consonant words having a different meaning (Fig. 12). This testifies to a profound pathological state of the system of verbal connections in oligophrenic children.

Could we expect under such conditions to obtain in oligophrenic children the same correlation between the immediate and the verbal systems which is observed in children with the cerebro-asthenic syndrome? Could we also expect that the constantly inhibited cerebral cortex of profound oligophrenics would allow us to utilize their defective speech as a compensatory remedy?

Experiments carried out in our laboratory by V. I. Lubovsky, A. I. Meshcheryakov and E. N. Martsinovsky have given a negative answer to these questions. They have shown that the process of formation of new temporary connections in profound oligophrenics is characterized by weakness, disequilibrium and inertness of the nervous processes, which is such a characteristic trait of the higher nervous activity in such subjects. Its specific feature consists in the fact that the speech system does not here participate so actively in the

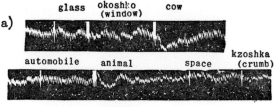

glass   okoshko (window)   cow

a)

automobile   animal   space   kzoshka (crumb)

okoshko

b)   flower   (window)   dog

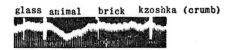

glass   animal   brick   kzoshka (crumb)

A. Normal child. (a) Svetl.Sh., 13.0; (b) Marina A., 11.0.
After the word "Koshka" (cat) was reinforced, - all words
with a semantic connexion (animal, dog, etc) give plethysmographic reaction (constriction of the vessels of the
finger); words with acoustic likeness (okoshko = window,
kroshka = crumb) do not give any reaction.

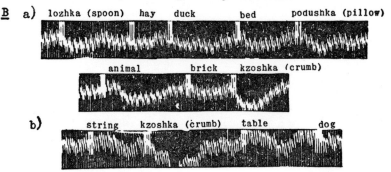

B a) lozhka (spoon)   hay   duck   bed   podushka (pillow)

animal   brick   kzoshka (crumb)

b)   string   kzoshka (crumb)   table   dog

B. Oligophrenic child. (a) Lucy S., 16.0 (oligophrenic)
(b) V.B., 13.0 (oligophrenic). Under the same conditions-
words with semantic connections (with the word "cat")
(animal, dog etc.) don't give any reaction, or give sometimes slight reaction: words with acoustic likeness
(lozhka - spoon, podushza - pillow, kroska - crumb) give
a vessel constriction (after O. Vinogradova).

Fig. 12

Plethysmographic reactions to verbal signals in normal
and oligophrenic children

formation of new connections as in normal children of the same age.

Whereas in the course of elaboration of the simplest systems of reactions (for example, of positive motor reactions to red signals and of inhibitory reactions to green signals) these subjects are still able to formulate the necessary generalizations and to give a correct account of their actions, the picture essentially changes as soon as we complicate the task and begin to elaborate in them reactions which require a preliminary separation of the signalling properties. In these cases—for example, when we try to elaborate a system consisting of positive reactions to a long signal and inhibitory reactions to a short signal of the same color, or of positive reactions to each third signal of a series of similar signals— the system of the verbal connections of the subject, which is extremely unstable and imperfect, proves unable to separate the required signalling property; the system of connections is here elaborated very slowly, unconsciously, by way of a gradual concentration of diffuse excitation. It needs constant reinforcement, disappears with the discontinuance of the latter and after a long process, finally leads to the elaboration of a motor stereotype, which only externally resembles an effective system of reactions and whose true nature can be disclosed if we somewhat change the conditions of the experiment. Fig. 13 presents such an example; it shows how a short delay in the presentation of the stimuli transforms the previously elaborated system of reactions to each third signal. Thus it convincingly proves that actually we deal here

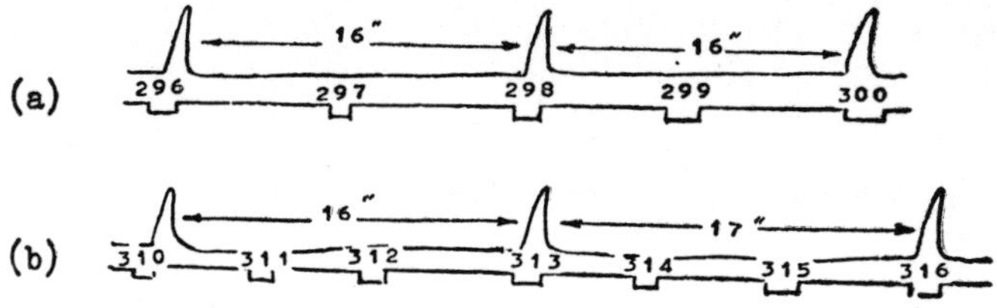

Khrom. 11 yrs. (Oligophrenia)

Fig. 13

Inertness of motor reaction in an oligophrenic child

not with reactions to abstract numbers of the signals, but with an elementary reflex to time, which alone stimulates this complex motor system. The inability verbally to formulate the principle of the motor reactions, which is characteristic of oligophrenic children, confirms the fact that in these cases the system of the verbal connections really does not take part in the formation of motor reactions.

However, the insufficient participation of the speech system in the formation of new connections in oligophrenic children is explained not only by their qualitative defects, but also by the neurodynamic defects of the connections of the verbal system, which are—as shown by V. I. Lubovsky— *much more inert* than connections elaborated directly in the motor sphere. This is expressed in the fact that a profound oligophrenic will continue, long after he has transformed one system of *motor* reactions into another (for example, producing a positive reaction to a short signal and an inhibitory reaction to a long signal) to retain the old *verbal* connection. He will still say that he presses the balloon at the appearance of the long signal and abstains from pressing it in response to the short signal. Sometimes this inertness of the verbal pattern is of an even more pronounced character; we observed many children who after the transition from this system of reactions to a new one and after the elaboration of a system of pressures to each second signal, continued inertly to repeat that they "press to a long signal and do not press to a short one," although the signals no longer differed in duration.

Can we, then, expect that any attempts to use the structurally defective and dynamically inert speech as a regulatory mechanism will bring about a more or less appreciable effect?

Experiments carried out with this aim show quite the opposite. They give convincing proofs that in profound forms of oligophrenia the child's own speech cannot serve as a "control mechanism" whose strengthening would successfully compensate for his general neurodynamical defects, as is the case in children with the cerebro-asthenic syndrome. Playing no definite role in the formation of the temporary connections manifesting strongly pronounced neurodynamical defects, and being extremely inert, the child's own speech usually does not perform any regulatory function and sometimes even hinders the normal course of the reactions which have been elaborated in the child.

We can illustrate this by a few simple facts.

If (as was shown by V. I. Lubovsky) after the elaboration in a profound oligophrenic of a stable system of differentiated motor reactions (for example, a reaction of pressure in response to a red signal and that of inhibition of movement in response to a green signal) the experimenter replaced the visual signal by a corresponding word ("Red!" or "Green!") the previously elaborated differentiation disappeared; the subject began to respond to all signals without exception, manifestly reacting to the sounding of the word and not connecting its meaning with the already elaborated system. If under such conditions (as shown by the observations of E. N. Martsinovskaya), after the elaboration of a well-established system of motor reactions (for example, of pressures in response to short signals and inhibition of the motor reactions in response to long signals) the experimenter asked the child to react to the same signals with corresponding words (by saying "Press!" in response to the former and "Don't press!" in response to the latter signals) the subject again did not apply the previously elaborated habit to his verbal reactions; he began in a stereotyped fashion to repeat one and the same word, or to alternate his responses by repeating the words "Press!" and "Don't press!" in succession, irrespective of the character of the given signal. Sometimes the inertness of the verbal system is so great that the subject begins to manifest in his verbal reactions even worse results, gradually increasing the perseveration of a certain link of the verbal response. These two facts are shown in Fig. 14.

Is not this a sufficient proof that the verbal reaction of an oligophrenic child, which has little connection with the main motor reaction, and which is inert and easily loses its initial

A

(a)

(b)   yes!   yes!   yes!   yes! yes!   yes!

Laza F. 14 yrs. (imbecile) (after Martsinovkaya)

Inertness in motor and verbal reaction
in an oligophrenic child

B

no! no!   yes!   no!   no!   yes!   no!   no! no!   yes!
           no!   no!

no!   no!   no!   no! no!   yes!

no! no! no! no!   no!   no! no! no! no!   yes!

Vlad B. R.   14 yrs. 6 mths. (imbecile)

The child gives extra-signal motor (a) and verbal (b)
reaction to the light stimuli

Fig. 14

The A imbecile child gives verbal perseverations in
system to respond to every third signal

    (a) Motor reactions (to press to every
        third signal)

    (b) Verbal reactions (to answer no-no-yes)

function, cannot serve as a mechanism of self-regulation and cannot compensate for his defects as it does in the case of the previously considered group of pathological states?

However, if we tried to perform on oligophrenic children experiments with the combination of verbal and motor reactions in the same way as described above, we should see that two more factors hinder the effective influence of speech on the course of the motor reactions.

The first of these factors is the difficulty with which the complex functional systems are elaborated—a difficulty which is peculiar to the pathological cerebral cortex of an oligophrenic child. It is precisely this difficulty which impedes the very combination of the motor and verbal reactions in profound oligophrenics: they find it hard to synchronize both reactions since the verbal reactions are not connected with the motor reactions, they either precede them or, on the contrary, are retarded; and very soon it can be observed that the two isolated series of reactions, which do not form a single functional system, begin to inhibit each other owing to negative induction. As a result, the less consolidated (verbal or motor) reaction *begins to disappear* (Fig. 15). It is quite natural that this fact makes the regulatory influence of speech impossible.

The second factor preventing the verbal reaction of an oligophrenic child from acting as a regulatory agent is connected with the defective structure of the speech itself.

We have already mentioned that speech is always a complex stimulus consisting both of non-specific (impelling or

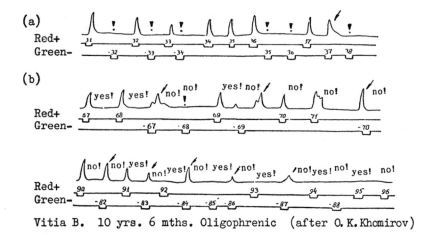

Vitia B. 10 yrs. 6 mths. Oligophrenic (after O. K. Khomirov)

Fig. 15

Negative role of speech in establishing of motor reactions
in an oligophrenic child

The child has to press the balloon after every red
signal and inhibit motor reactions after every
green one

    (a) Motor reactions. (A fairly well elaborated
        system of reactions)

    (b) Combined (verbal + motor) reactions. (Dis-
        inhibition of motor reactions to negative
        signals. General inhibition of reactions
        to the end of the experimental series)

inhibiting) and specific (elective and significative) components; we have also seen that in the course of evolution the
former gradually recede to the background and give way to
the latter which begin to play a leading, predominant role.

The specific feature characterizing the derangement of the

140

functional systems in oligophrenics consists precisely in the fact that this predominance of elective (abstracting and generalizing) verbal connections is here not sufficiently strong. Consequently the primitive, non-specific functions of speech easily begin to take the upper hand. Therefore, even if we succeed in obtaining correct verbal responses from our subject as a result of long training, it in no way means that we shall also obtain their proper regulatory action; while responding to the inhibitory signal with the correct verbal reaction "Don't press!", our subject will not inhibit his motor reaction; he will, on the contrary, in response to the non-specific, stimulatory influence of the verbal response, disinhibit it. Only if we bring the verbal and motor reactions into full innervation conformity (i.e., if we make the subject say the word "Press!" and simultaneously press the balloon in response to the positive signal, and be silent simultaneously abstaining from any pressures in response to the inhibitory signal), *can we obtain the necessary effect* (Fig. 16).

This last fact leads us to a conclusion which goes beyond questions of the neurodynamics and is of great general psychological significance.

Pathological changes in the activity of the cerebral cortex which are peculiar to oligophrenia considerably disturb the general mental development of the child; as a result, the formation of normal speech activity, whose regulatory function has been described by us in the process of its development, does not take place here; speech, deprived of the rich and

141

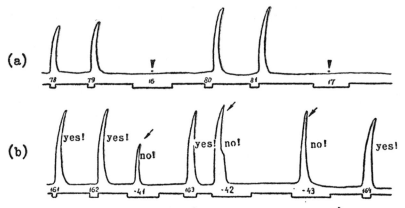

Bal. 14 yrs. (imbecile) (after Martsinovskaya)

Fig. 16

Disinhibition of motor reactions under influence of
speech in an oligophrenic child

The child has to press the balloon after every short
signal and inhibit motor reactions after every long
signal.

    (a) Motor reactions (fairly well elaborated
        system)

    (b) Combined (verbal and motor) reactions (dis-
        inhibition of motor reactions under the
        influence of child's own verbal answer

mobile system of elective connections, which normally are
already dominant at the age of six, cannot here play the role
of the "highest regulator of human behavior" and turn man
into the "highest self-regulating system" of which Pavlov
spoke in the last years of his life.

Our exposition would be incomplete if we did not touch,

142

even though briefly, upon a new series of investigations which may be of considerable interest to us.

So far, we have deliberately dealt with changes taking place in the regulatory influence of speech in cases of more or less diffuse pathological states of the cerebral cortex. But will not our principle prove applicable also to the analysis of *local pathology* of the brain? Can we assume that among the functionally diverse areas of the cerebral cortex there are some whose lesion leaves the regulatory function of speech fully unaffected, and, on the other hand, some whose lesion leads to considerable derangements precisely of the regulatory function of speech?

Investigations aimed at the elucidation of these questions were started not long ago, but they have already yielded clear, although somewhat unexpected results. They have shown that lesions of certain zones of speech (in particular, of the temporal area of the left hemisphere) derange the auditory analysis and synthesis and entail disturbances in the acoustic structure of speech; however, they do not lead to an appreciable derangement of its regulatory function: the patient continues successfully to apply his acoustically defective speech to the regulation of his deranged neurodynamics.

On the other hand, severe lesions of the frontal lobes of the brain, externally not accompanied by an aphasic phenomenon, lead (as shown in our laboratory by N. A. Filippicheva, B. G. Spirin, A. I. Meshcheryakov and M. P. Ivanova) to a considerable dissociation of the two signalling systems and to a strongly pronounced derangement of the regulatory function of speech. The establishment of the basic laws which determine the local pathology of the regulatory function of speech is still a matter for future investigation; and there is no doubt that this series of investigations will make it possible to approach anew a number of old problems relating to the theory of aphasia and of the local pathology of the brain.

❋   ❋   ❋

We have concluded the summary exposition of the facts which have been obtained by us as a result of a series of investigations carried out in recent years.

A thorough study of the role of speech in the organization of human behavior, which was the subject of our research, shows that the "second signalling system" (according to Pavlov's terminology), constituting an essential feature of the human higher nervous activity, provides great possibilities for a closer understanding of the mechanisms of the mental processes and of regulation of human behavior.

There is every reason to believe that the speech system, which is formed in the process of the child's social intercourse with the adult, is a powerful means of systemic organization of our mental processes, and that the precise study of this will help us to solve the highly important task of modifying and perfecting the higher nervous activity of man; consequently, it can help us to approach the solution of the basic task of psychology—to make known the scientific foundations of the organization of human behavior.

References

ABRAMYAN, L. A. Organization of the voluntary activity of the child with the help of verbal instruction. A diploma thesis in the Department of Psychology, Moscow University (1955).

ANOKHIN, P. K. Peculiarities of the afferent apparatus of a conditioned reflex. *Vopr. psikh.*, No. 6 (1955).

BERNSTEIN, N. A. The structure of movements, Moscow (1947).

ELKONIN, D. B. Peculiarities of the interaction between the first and second signalling systems in children of pre-school age. *Trud. Akad. Ped. Nauk RSFSR*, Vol. 64 (1954).

ELKONIN, D. B. Psychological problems of pre-school games. Problems of the psychology of children of pre-school age. *Trud. Akad. Ped. Nauk RSFSR* (1948).

GALPERIN, N. Y. The formation of sensory images and concepts. Proceedings of Psychological Conference, Moscow (1956).

KHOMSKAYA, E. D. Contribution to the question of the role of speech in the compensation of motor reactions. Problems of the higher nervous activity of normal and abnormal children, Moscow (1956).

KHOMSKAYA, E. D. The dynamics of the latent periods of motor reactions in children. *Trud. Akad. Ped. Nauk RSFSR*, Vol. 1 (1956).

IVANOV-SMOLENSKY, A. G. Interrelations between the first and second signalling systems under certain physiological and pathological conditions. *Fiz. zh. SSSR*, Vol. 35 (1949).

IVANOV-SMOLENSKY, A. G. Study of the joint activity of the first and second signalling systems. *Zh. vyssh. nervn. deyatel.* No. 1 (1951).

145

REFERENCES

KOLTZOVA, M. M. The formation of signalling systems in children. Thesis, Leningrad (1953).

KISLYUK, T. A. Contribution to the question of formation of motor habits in children of pre-school age. *Vopr. psikh.*, No. 6 (1956).

LEONT'EV, A. N. The development of memory, Moscow (1932).

LEONT'EV, A. N. Formation et Nature des propriétés et de processes psychiques de l'Homme. XIV. Congrès International de Psychologie, Montreal.

LUBOVSKII, V. I. Some peculiarities of the higher nervous activity in oligophrenic children. Problems of higher nervous activity in normal and abnormal children, Moscow (1957).

LURIA, A. R. The nature of human conflicts, New York (1932).

LURIA, A. R. Restoration of the functions of the brain after war traumas, U.S.S.R. Academy of Medical Sciences, Moscow (1942).

LURIA, A. R. (ed.) Problems of the higher nervous activity of normal and abnormal child, Academy of Pedagogical Science Press, Moscow, Vol. I (1956); Vol. II (1958).

LYUBLINSKAYA, A. A. The role of the tongue in the mental development of the child. *Trud. Herz. ped. inst.*, Vol. 112, Leningrad (1955).

MANUILENKO, Z. V. The development of voluntary behavior in children of pre-school age. *Trud. Akad. Ped. Nauk RSFSR*, Vol. 14 (1948).

MARUSEVA, A. M. and CHISTOVICH, L. A. Modifications in the activity of the auditory analyser under the influence of verbal instructions. *Zh. vyssh. nervn. deyatel.*, Vol. 4, No. 4 (1954).

MARTSINOVSKAYA, E. N. Research into the reflective and regulatory role of the second signalling system in pre-school age. Collected Papers of the Department of Psychology, Moscow University.

MESHCHERYAKOV, A. I. The role of previous experience in the elaboration of new connections in Man. *Vopr. psikh.*, No. 3 (1955).

REFERENCES

MESHCHERYAKOV, A. I. The participation of the second signalling system in the analysis and synthesis of chain stimuli in normal and mentally backward children. Problems of higher nervous activity of normal and abnormal children, Moscow (1956).

MINSKAYA, G. I. The transition from visual-active to reasoning thought in children of pre-school age. Thesis, Moscow (1954).

NEVEROVICH, Y. Z. The mastery of object movement in infancy and in pre-school age. *Trud. Akad. Ped. Nauk RSFSR,* Vol. 14 (1948).

NOVIKOVA, L. A. Investigation of the electrical activity of the brain in oligophrenics. Problems of higher nervous activity of normal and abnormal children, Moscow (1956).

ORBELI, L. A. Lectures on the physiology of the nervous system, Moscow and Leningrad (1935).

PAVLOV, I. P. Twenty years of study of the higher nervous activity (behavior) of animals. Complete Works, Vol. 4, Moscow (1951).

PAVLOV, I. P. The Pavlovian "Wednesday" Gatherings, Vol. II and III (1951).

PARAMONOVA, N. P. The formation of interaction between the two signalling systems in normal children. Problems of higher nervous activity of normal and abnormal children, Moscow (1956).

ROSENGARDT, G. L. Speech and development of perception, Moscow (1947).

VINOGRADOVA, O. S. Some peculiarities of the orienting reactions to stimulations of the second signalling system in normal and mentally backward school-children. *Vopr. psikh.,* No. 6 (1955).

VINOGRADOVA, O. S. The dependence of the orienting reflex on the intensity of the stimulus. *Vopr. psikh.,* No. 2 (1955).

VYGOTSKII, L. S. Selected psychological works. Academy of Pedagogical Sciences, Moscow (1956).

REFERENCES

YENDOVITSKAYA, T. V. The role of speech in the accomplishment of simple actions by children of pre-school age. *Trud. Akad. Ped. Nauk RSFSR*, Vol. 64 (1954).

ZANKOV, L. V. Memory (1949).

ZAPOROZHETS, A. V. The development of voluntary movements. *Vopr. psikh.*, No. 1 (1955).

ZAPOROZHETS, A. V. The problem of voluntary movements in the light of the works of I. M. Sechenov. *Vopr. psikh.*, No. 1 (1956).

ZISSLINA, N. N. Electrophysiological investigation of the functional state of the brain of oligophrenics by the method of rhythmic optical stimulations. Problems of higher nervous activity in normal and abnormal children, Moscow (1956).